4.35

285% M N + 50/nn

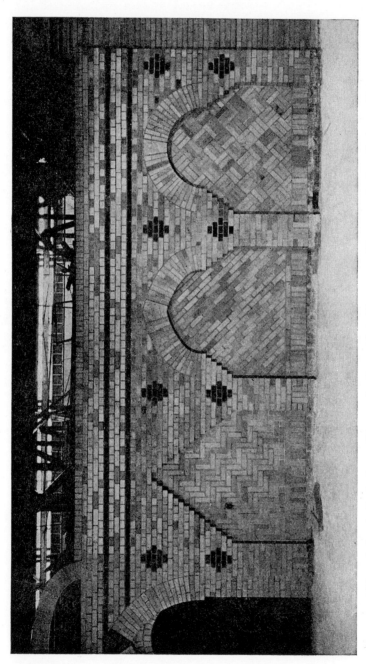

These Arches, in the Arabesque Manner, Are Geometric in Character and Represent the Best Craftsmanship.
The Ornamental Inlays Are Usually of Glazed Brick in Contrasting Color

Detroit Building Trades School, Detroit, Michigan

BRICKLAYING

SKILL AND PRACTICE

by

J. RALPH DALZELL

Building and Construction Specialist

and

GILBERT TOWNSEND

*Member of Ross, Patterson, Townsend, and
Heughan, Architects and Engineers, Montreal, Canada*

Co-authors of

HOW TO PLAN A HOUSE
HOW TO REMODEL A HOUSE
MASONRY SIMPLIFIED

Illustrations by

ARTHUR E. BURKE

*Head, Illustration Department, American Technical
Society*

(Revised Edition)

AMERICAN TECHNICAL SOCIETY

Chicago, U. S. A.

PREFACE

THERE ARE TWO WAYS of training brick masons. One method of instruction requires a personal demonstration of the craft to the pupil. The second method introduces a clearly written text, together with an abundant use of illustrations, to show trainees the on-the-job procedures of a skilled craftsman.

Bricklaying Skill and Practice uses the second of these two excellent methods because its authors fully realize that it is impossible to guide each hand in order to teach the manipulative skill of laying bricks. They are convinced, however, that the effective use of illustrations and the clear text material found in *Bricklaying Skill and Practice* can be used not only by the beginner, but also by the more advanced mason as well.

The beginner will find information to help him perfect his new craft. In order to help the newcomer to bricklaying, a study has been made of those difficulties that usually stump him. For the professional mason, attention has been given to those universal practices which provide short cuts and improve efficiency.

Bricklaying Skill and Practice can be used not only by the learner for a trade and by the professional mason, but it will also be of invaluable help to anyone who hopes to do an occasional job on his home or on his farm. The contractor, the builder, and the architect, too, will find this volume to be of great value on his reference shelf. Those who want specific information about fireplaces and chimneys will find complete directions for their construction in Chapters V and VI.

Since this book was first published, much attention has been given to the development of through-the-wall brick units for the construction of one-story single-family residences. For this revised edition, detailed information about this popular method of home building has been added. Chapter VII is devoted to the discussion of a representative product.

If building with bricks is, or is likely to become, a part of your working life, *Bricklaying Skill and Practice* is for you.

THE PUBLISHERS

ACKNOWLEDGMENTS

The authors gratefully acknowledge the wholehearted co-operation of the following individuals and organizations:

G. J. Fink, Executive Secretary, Oxychloride Cement Association, Washington, D.C.

Hilmer Forsgren, Mason Contractor, Chicago, Illinois

R. Hunter Cochran, Ohio Brick and Tile Institute, Canton, Ohio

F. L. McCrea, Adel Clay Products Company, Des Moines, Iowa

S. Walter Stauffer, President, National Lime Association, Washington, D.C.

Herman Marks, General Contractor, Chicago, Illinois

J. J. Cermak, Structural Clay Products Institute, Washington, D.C.

W. D. M. Allen, Portland Cement Association, Chicago, Illinois

Harry C. Plummer, Structural Clay Products Institute, Washington, D.C.

W. A. Arter, The Jaeger Machine Company, Columbus, Ohio

Earl L. Bedell, Divisional Director, Detroit School Board, Detroit, Michigan

Louisville Cement Company, Louisville, Kentucky

Detroit Building Trades School, Detroit, Michigan

The Colonial Fireplace Company, Chicago, Illinois

U.S. Department of Commerce, Washington, D.C.

National Concrete Masonry Association, Chicago, Illinois

Clay Products Institute, Des Moines, Iowa

U.S. Gypsum Company, Chicago, Illinois

National Homes Foundation, Washington, D.C.

Merry Brothers Brick and Tile Company, Augusta, Georgia

U.S. Department of Agriculture, Washington, D.C.

The Belden Brick Company, Canton, Ohio

John J. Hassett, Structural Clay Products Institute, Washington, D.C.

CONTENTS

Erecting an Arch for a Window or Door Opening

Note the wood center form which lends support to the arch while construction is in progress. In building arches, only sure methods will produce good results.

Detroit Building Trades School, Detroit, Michigan

CHAPTER I

Brick Masonry

DEFINITION AND DESCRIPTION OF BRICK MASONRY

The term *brick masonry* should be applied only to that type of construction employing comparatively small building units made of burned clay or shale. There are bricks made of other materials but when such bricks are used in masonry work, the term brick masonry should not be employed. The standard physical properties for bricks used in brick masonry structural work are set forth by the United States Government and by the American Society for Testing Materials in what are known as *Federal* and *Standard Specifications* for brick masonry.

Ordinary brick are economical in cost and when hard-burned and laid in good mortar are one of the most durable construction materials now in use. Bricks are comparatively small in size and are therefore easy to handle. Since they are thoroughly burned during their manufacture, they can be used in construction work intended to be fire-resistive as well as in other forms of permanent construction.

BRICK MANUFACTURING

The raw materials in the form of clays or shales from which burned bricks are made are found in all parts of the country. Clays are produced naturally by the weathering of rocks. Shales are produced naturally in practically the same way and from the same material, but differ from clays in that the shale has been compressed, and, in some cases heated, producing a material that is much more dense than clay, and consequently more difficult to remove from banks or pits. The chemical composition of clay or shale and the method of firing them give the various colors and textures to bricks. The colors vary from a light cream to very dark red, with red, buff, and cream predominating.

Clay and shale are dug or quarried and in some cases allowed to weather in the open for a period of time. The purpose of this weathering is to allow the material to break down naturally into a workable mass. Brick plants are usually located near the source of the raw material. Since the process of brick manufacturing is uninterrupted, the raw materials must be dug or quarried continuously so that delivery to the brick plant will be constant. If the clay or shale delivered to the plant contains the proper ingredients, it is a simple process to grind, mix, and mold the bricks preparatory to firing. However, it is necessary sometimes to mix two or more kinds of shale, clay, or other ingredients in order to produce a mixture of the proper consistency.

Methods of Molding Bricks. There are several methods of molding bricks. Among these are the stiff-mud, soft-mud, and dry-press processes. Each process requires slightly different molding equipment and treatment in mixing. The shale or clay must be ground and mixed to the proper consistency for molding and the correct amount of water added.

STIFF-MUD PROCESS. In the stiff-mud process of forming and molding, the clay is delivered to an auger machine which forces the plastic mass through a die in a continuous stream called a column. The die molds the mass into the desired shape for brick and as the column is extruded, it passes through a machine which cuts it into the desired lengths.

SOFT-MUD PROCESS. In the soft-mud process, machines press the clay into forms rather than extrude it from a die. The final results are the same as in the stiff-mud process.

DRY-PRESS PROCESS. The dry-press process permits the use of more or less nonplastic and relative dry clays. The clay is put into molds and subjected to pressure of from 550 to 1,500 pounds per square inch.

Drying of the Molded Shapes. An important part of the manufacture of bricks is the drying of the molded shapes. It is necessary to evaporate a large amount of the water in the molded bricks to assure greater strength. The more thoroughly the bricks are dried, the easier it is to stack them properly in the kilns.

Molded bricks are usually dried in ovens which are heated. The bricks remain in these ovens for two or three days' time depending upon the amount of moisture which must be evaporated.

Burning of the Molded Shapes. The kilns used to burn the bricks are actually large ovens. The bricks are stacked in the kilns in such a manner that ample space is left so that flames may circulate freely. Between 75 and 100 hours is required generally for the complete process, including the cooling of the bricks. Kilns must be heated gradually to drive off any remaining moisture in the bricks. This stage in the burning process is known as *water smoking*. The temperature, after water smoking, is gradually raised until it reaches the vitrification point—the point at which the materials composing the bricks begin to fuse.

After firing, the heated bricks are gradually cooled to avoid checking of their surfaces.

KINDS OF BRICK

There are many kinds of brick. Some of them are different in formation and composition, while others vary according to the use to which they may be put. Some are made for economy, some for strength, some for appearance, and some for special uses, such as for fireplaces. The kinds of brick most commonly encountered are explained in the paragraphs that follow. It should be repeated that brick specifications can be obtained that will serve as a guide for selecting and purchasing brick for any purpose.

Common Brick. The term common brick is applied to bricks made of ordinary clays or shales and burned in the usual manner in kilns. Such brick do not have special scorings or markings and are not produced in any special color or surface texture.

There are grades of common brick which vary in different parts of the country. In some localities, all the brick coming from the kilns are sold without any grading even though there may be a difference in their hardness and strength. In other localities, the bricks are graded and sold as front and back bricks. The front bricks are those burned to the greatest degree of hardness. Common brick is also known as hard and *kiln-run* brick. When bricks are overburned in the kiln, they are called clinkers. Such bricks are unusually hard and durable. Because of the way in which the heat is applied in some types of kilns, the bricks are classified according to their position in the kiln. Typical classifications are *arch, clinker, red, well-burned, soft, salmon, rough-hard, straight-hard,* and *stretcher.*

Arch and clinker bricks are those which have been overburned and are thus extremely hard and durable. These bricks may be slightly irregular in shape and size.

Red, well-burned, and straight-hard are well-burned, hard, and durable. Stretcher brick are selected from these classifications as the most uniform in hardness, size, and durability.

Rough-hard brick correspond to the clinker classification.

Soft and salmon brick are those which were farthest from the fire in the kiln and are therefore underburned, soft, and not as durable as the other classifications described. It should be pointed out that in certain localities the existing clay is of such composition that hard and durable bricks are salmon in color.

There may be other classifications or names for common brick. However, the important thing is to determine the hardness and durability of the bricks before they are laid up as structural work.

Face Brick. This kind of brick is made of especially selected materials in order that colors and textures can be controlled, and so that hardness, size uniformity, and strength are all of high classification. These bricks may have various markings or surface finishes.

Pressed Brick. Both common and face brick may be classified as pressed brick, depending on the materials used, their coloring, and burning. The dry-press process is used to make this class of brick which has regular smooth faces, sharp edges, and perfectly square corners. Ordinarily, all pressed brick are used as face brick.

Firebrick. This kind of brick is made from a special type of fire clay which will stand the high temperatures found in fireplaces, furnaces, etc., without cracking or decomposing. Firebrick is generally larger than regular structural brick and often hand-molded.

Glazed Brick. This type of brick has one surface of each brick glazed in white or any other color desired.

Imitation Brick. This kind of brick is similar to common brick in size and use but is made of Portland cement and sand. They are not burned but have the same qualities as good cement mortar.

PHYSICAL CHARACTERISTICS OF BRICK

Size of Brick. The United States Bureau of Standards recommends that brick sizes should be as shown in Table I.

Rough-faced brick are those which have been formed so that their faces are irregular. Smooth-faced brick are those whose surfaces are smooth like pressed brick. Most face brick are of the latter type.

TABLE I. STANDARD BRICK SIZES*

KIND	DEPTH INCHES	WIDTH INCHES	LENGTH INCHES
Common..	2¼	3¾	8
Rough-faced.............................	2¼	3¾	8
Smooth-faced.............................	2¼	3⅞	8

* Permissible variables are: plus or minus 1/16″ in depth, ⅛″ in width, and ¼″ in length.

Weight of Brick. The weight of brick varies because of the materials used in their manufacture, the amount of burning, and their sizes. Since every manufacturer produces brick of different weight, such information should be obtained directly from him. An approximate weight, especially of common brick, is about 4½ pounds each.

Quality of Brick. Brick should be uniform in shape and size; their edges should be fairly square, straight, and well defined; they should be free of cracks, pebbles, twists, and broken corners; and should be well burned but not vitrified or brittle. A good test of bricks is to strike two of them together. They should emit a metallic ring. Surfaces should not be too smooth because some roughness is required to assure good bonding with the mortar. A good brick should not absorb more than 10 to 15 per cent of its weight in water after having been soaked in water for 24 hours.

Colors and Surface Finishes of Brick. In general, the brick produced in the United States from natural clays and shales without special mixing are red in color. There are a few localities where the materials available produce bricks which tend to be yellow. The slight difference in the clays and shales and the manufacturing processes account for these various shades of red and yellow. Some difference in color also is possible between burnings which make it advisable to purchase enough bricks for a job all at one time to assure the same coloring.

Such minerals as iron, lime, and magnesia are responsible for the coloring in bricks. These minerals occur naturally in the clays and shales. For example, iron in clay will produce yellow, orange, red, and blue. Magnesia produces a brown color. When the manufacturer carefully controls the amounts of these minerals, he can produce bricks of almost any desired color provided he also controls the amount of heat in the kiln. Kiln heat also plays an important part in the production of colors.

Many surface textures in face bricks are possible by various steps in the manufacturing. For example, rough textures can be obtained by mixing coarse materials with the other brick materials or wires can be used to cut the bricks as they are extruded from a die. Wire cutting produces a type of finish or texture which is pleasing to the eye.

There are many possible textures produced. Brick manufacturers will supply literature relative to their products free of charge. Such literature can be used in selecting texture.

HOW BRICKS ARE USED

Bricks can be and are used for many structural purposes, including all kinds of walls and partitions, footings and foundations, columns, pilasters, chimneys and fireplaces, furnaces, sidewalks and steps, floors, garden walls, arches over wall openings, parapets, and pavements. The possible uses of brick are practically unlimited.

Common Brick. Generally, this kind of brick is used for the backing courses in solid or cavity brick walls. The harder and more durable kinds are preferable for this purpose. If a wall is to have a stucco exterior finish, a good grade of common brick can be used for all tiers. In some cases, selected and well-burned common brick in various shades of red or tan are used as face brick with good results.

The softer common brick, such as the salmon classification, should not be used for backing or as face brick in any wall or other structure which must support heavy loads. These softer brick should be used only in partitions or other walls which have no appreciable weight to support and where they are not exposed to the weather.

Good grades of common brick can be used for garden walls, sidewalks, columns, piers, steps, and other such typical construction, with good results.

Face Brick. This kind of brick is used generally for all veneering and exterior tiers in outside walls and chimneys of residences and other buildings. Sometimes face brick are used only in those exterior tiers which are visible from the street. In such cases, those exterior tiers not visible from the street should be laid up using well-burned common brick. This kind of brick also can be used for garden walls, walks, and steps, where exceptionally good appearance is desired.

Pressed Brick. As previously explained, both common and face brick can be of the *pressed* brick classification. However, while many types of face brick are produced by this process, only the better grades of common brick are of the pressed-brick variety. Pressed brick make excellent face brick for exterior tiers of solid or cavity walls and for veneering. This kind of brick is especially useful when exact dimensions are desired in walls or other structural members. They can be classified the same as face brick unless specifically described as common brick.

Firebrick. These brick should be used only to line the interior surfaces of fireplaces, boiler furnaces, etc., where extreme heat is encountered.

Glazed Brick. These brick, because their exposed surfaces are glazed, make excellent exterior tiers for walls or partitions in dairies, hospitals, and other buildings where cleanliness and ease of cleaning is an important factor.

Imitation Brick. This kind of brick can be used any place where the usual common, pressed, or face brick can be used.

There are many other uses for the various kinds and grades of brick, all or any of which can be discussed with building material dealers or manufacturers.

BONDING AND TYPES OF BONDS

In order that walls, partitions, chimneys, and other structural members will be strong, solid, and durable, it is necessary that the brick be placed in such a manner that they are all tied together to form a cohesive block or mass. The mortar in the horizontal and vertical joints tends to tie all brick together but unless the individual brick is placed and bonded properly, a wall, for example, will not have much strength or durability, especially when it supports heavy loads. The process of tying a wall or other unit masonry structure together is called *bonding*. Good bonding is accomplished only by lapping one brick across or over at least two other bricks in the course below it. This method is also known as breaking joints.

Mortar on the Boards Should Be Kept Well Tempered with Water.
Louisville Cement Company, Louisville, Kentucky

Mortar Should Be Plastic Enough To Enable the Bricklayer to
Properly Bed the Brick and Fill the Joints
Louisville Cement Company, Louisville, Kentucky

Fig. 1 shows an 8″ brick wall which is improperly bonded. In this wall, the bricks are placed so that the wall is merely a series of piers or columns that abut each other. In the illustration these piers or columns are numbered on top *1, 2, 3, 4,* and *5*. There is no bond between them except the mortar in the joints *AB, CD, EF, GH,* etc. While the mortar does hold the piers or columns together, it is not sufficient to make the wall a solid, cohesive mass as is necessary. A wall built in this manner would, when loaded, crack open along the

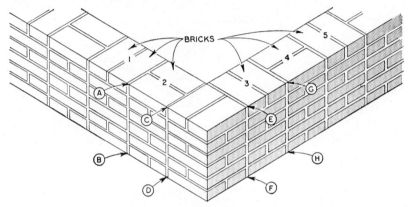

Fig. 1. Improperly Bonded Brick Wall

joints previously mentioned, thus losing much of its strength and durability. It would not be structurally safe or dependable for any type of construction.

Fig. 2 shows an 8″ brick wall which is properly bonded. Note that each of the stretchers rests on two bricks in the course below and that the vertical joints are not continuous but are broken from course to course. When headers are laid up in such a wall, they, too, as illustrated in Fig. 2, rest on two bricks in the course below. It can be seen that proper bonding ties the wall together in both the direction of the length of the wall and in the direction of the height of the wall.

The foregoing explanation illustrates the principle and purpose of bonding. Several typical examples of bonding are explained and illustrated in the following pages.

Stretcher Bond. The bond shown in (A) of Fig. 3 is known as a *stretcher* bond because the bricks in all courses are laid as stretchers.

This bond is used extensively for brick veneering and for partitions which are only the thickness of a single tier of brick.

Header Bond.   The bond shown in (B) of Fig. 3 is known as *header* because the bricks in all courses are laid as headers. This bond can be used for walls or partitions 8″ thick.

Common Bond.   The bond shown in (C) of Fig. 3 is known as *common* bond and is perhaps the most generally used bond. It can be seen that every sixth course is a header course and the intervening

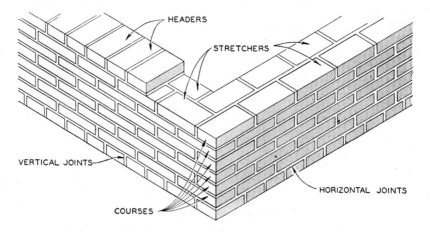

Fig. 2. Properly Bonded Brick Wall

courses are stretcher courses. Sometimes masons vary this bond to an extent by laying a header course every fourth or fifth course. This variation has a tendency to straighten the brickwork but for ordinary cases is not necessary. This bond is used extensively for building walls, especially when common brick are used, and for backing up stone, terra cotta, and face brick. It is also used to back up or face hollow tile and concrete block walls.

Old English Bond.   The bond shown in (D) of Fig. 3 is known as *Old English* bond and is one of the popular bonds used, especially for residence walls. This bond is produced by alternating a course of stretchers with a course of headers. A *closure* is laid next to the corner bricks in every course of headers.

Closures are parts of bricks used as a means of obtaining desired bonds at the corners of walls, as shown in (D) of Fig. 3. They are

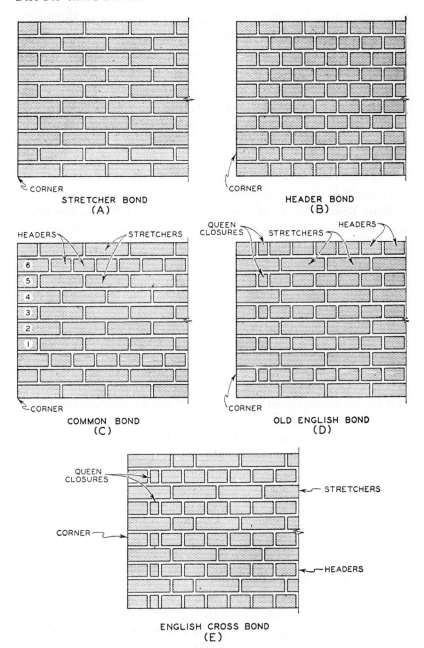

Fig. 3. Some Typical Bonds

often called *bats* instead of closures. If a brick is cut in half paralleling the long dimension, each half is called a queen closure. When a fourth of a brick is cut off, the remaining part is called a three-quarter bat or closure. When a brick is cut in half across the 3¾″ or 3⅞″ face, both halves are known as half-bats or closures. A one-quarter brick is known as a quarter-bat or closure. The closure shown in the Old English bond is a queen closure. Or, two quarter-closures may be used.

English Cross Bond.   The bond shown in (E) of Fig. 3 is known as *English Cross* bond. This bond differs only slightly from Old English bond. It is used where strength and beauty are required.

Dutch Bond.   The bond shown in (A) of Fig. 4 is known as *Dutch* bond. This bond is laid up using three-quarter and half closures together with regular headers and stretchers.

Flemish Bond (Double).   The bond shown in (B) of Fig. 4 is known as *Flemish Double* bond. It is laid up using queen or quarter-closures, headers, and stretchers.

The English, Dutch, and Flemish double bonds are rarely used in this country because of the care needed in their laying. However, they make beautiful strong walls.

Bonding Face Brick.   When face brick are laid as an exterior tier and backed by common brick, they must be bonded to the backing. This can be accomplished in two ways. If the facing bond has courses of headers, these headers can be face brick and bonded into the common bricks like any other header course. Or, if the face brick tier is laid in stretcher bond, such as in (A) of Fig. 3, metal ties must be used as anchors.

In (C) of Fig. 4 is shown a 12″ brick wall having face brick laid in stretcher bond and anchored to the backing by means of galvanized metal ties. These ties are spaced two or three bricks apart horizontally as part of the mortar joint. For best results they should be laid in at least every other course.

Soldier Courses.   A soldier course, as shown in (A) of Fig. 5, is composed of bricks embedded in walls so as to stand on end with only edges showing. Because of this upright position, such a course cannot be bonded into the wall of which it is a part. This has a tendency to weaken the wall, although not seriously.

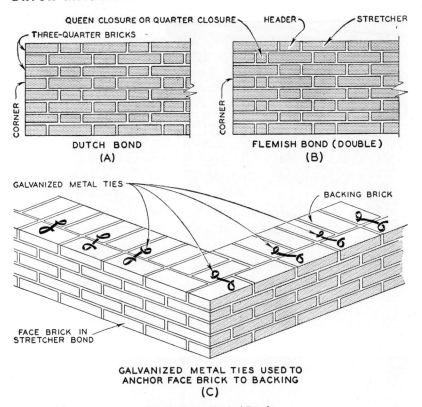

Fig. 4. Other Typical Bonds

Soldier courses are used mainly as a water table around a building at the level of the first floor. They are also used in laying flat arches on steel lintels over windows, doors, and other wall openings.

Rowlock Courses. A rowlock course, as shown in (B) of Fig. 5, is composed of bricks embedded in walls so as to lie on edge with only ends showing. Three rowlocks should be the same length as a stretcher in the face of a wall. Rowlocks are used as sills, borders, and parts of cornices and may be used also as coping and steps and in arches.

Good bonding without a doubt is one of the most important features of any brick masonry and therefore should be given the most careful attention by the masons doing the bricklaying. Careless work invariably results in walls or other structural parts which are unsightly, unsafe, and undependable from the standpoint of durability.

Mortar Is Carefully Spread with a Furrow Parallel
to the Length of the Brick

Detroit Building Trades School, Detroit, Michigan

The Trowel, the Edger, and the Spirit Level Are Essential
to the Brick Mason's Craft

Detroit Building Trades School, Detroit, Michigan

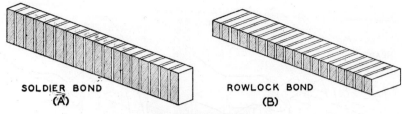

SOLDIER BOND   ROWLOCK BOND
(A)   (B)

Fig. 5. Typical Bonds

BRICKLAYING TOOLS

Bricklayers, unlike most other mechanics, need but few tools. Ordinarily, the following named and described tools are sufficient.

Plumb Rule. The plumb rule or spirit level is the tool necessary to guide the bricklayer in building walls or other structural parts, plumb and level. The modern plumb rule varies in length from 36″ to 48″ and is generally made of wood although metal is sometimes used in its construction. The better plumb rules have two level glasses at the center (midway between the two ends) and two plumb glasses near each end. These glasses are usually adjustable and well protected against breakage.

Such an instrument is a combination plumb rule and level. As a level, it is used in a horizontal position, in which case the glass at the center indicates the level. As a plumb rule, the tool is held with one edge against the brickwork and the upper of the two end glasses observed. No brick masonry can be laid without such a tool.

Trowels. The most important tools a bricklayer uses are his trowels. Typical trowels and their uses are illustrated in the how-to-lay-bricks section of this chapter. The large trowel, which is used most generally in ordinary bricklaying, is usually from 9″ to 11″ in length and from 4″ to 7″ or 8″ in its greatest width. The small trowel is generally from 4″ to 7″ in length and from 2″ to 4″ wide. For pointing work, some masons use an even smaller trowel which is from 3″ to 6″ in length and from 2″ to 3″ in width.

Brick Hammer. In order that a mason can make closures and bats as required in bonds and in other places such as around steel lintels, a peculiar kind of hammer is necessary as illustrated in (A) and (B) of Fig. 6. The hammer in this illustration is being used to make a queen closure. The first step, as shown at (A), is to make the cutting line all

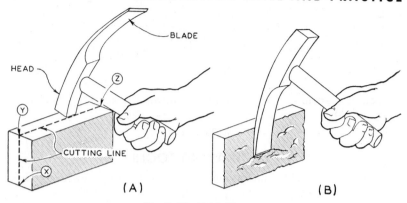

Fig. 6. The Brick Hammer

the way around the brick. This line is made by light blows of the hammer. When the line is complete, one sharp blow is given about as shown at (A), causing the brick to split. Rough places are trimmed, using the blade of the hammer as shown at (B). Cutting bricks cleanly and correctly requires a great deal of practice which can be had, using scrap bricks.

Brick Set. This tool, shown in Fig. 7, is used to cut bricks when more exact surfaces are required. The hammer is used to force this tool into the brick.

Jointer. This tool is used to make other than struck (explained in the following pages) joints. There are various kinds of such tools, all of which accomplish the same end. Their edges are rounded, pointed, etc., to make the required shape in the mortar as they are drawn along the joint.

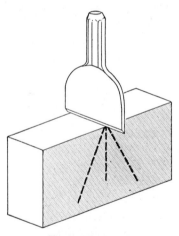

Fig. 7. The Brick Set

Line. The line is also an important tool. It is usually a stout piece of cord.

Square. This tool, which is the same as the carpenter's tool, is required for corners and in laying out walls.

In addition to the tools just described, miscellaneous items such as chalk, pencils, and knives can be found in the brick mason's tool kit.

Mortarboard. Most bricklayers prefer a mortarboard which is about three feet square. Sufficient quantities of mortar can be kept on a board of that size and there is ample space for the mortar to be worked by the bricklayer to keep it in the proper condition. Generally, mortar should be kept well rounded up rather than spread all over the board as this tends to prevent the formation of lumps in it.

MORTAR

Important Functions of Mortar. Ordinarily, mortar is thought of only as a means of bonding or sticking together, the bricks used in building walls and other brick masonry structural items. This is one of the most important functions of mortar. In addition to this, it forms a cushion which takes up all irregularities in the bricks and tends to distribute equally the weight or pressure in the various parts of, for example, a wall. This adds to the strength of brick masonry. Thus, mortar not only bonds all bricks together to form a solid mass but it also causes the mass to act with equal pressure throughout as in concrete.

There are other important functions of mortar which should not be overlooked. For example, it makes brick masonry largely water-proof and airproof. When all joints are properly made, a brick wall, in addition to supporting the building, also keeps out moisture and the dust and dirt carried in the air.

All mortar should be well mixed and neither too stiff nor too plastic. The degree of plasticity should be such as to make for easy working of the mortar with the trowel.

Properties of Mortar. The properties of mortar depend to a large extent upon the type of sand used in it. If the sand is *sharp, clean,* and *well screened,* the mortar should be excellent. When very fine sand is used, there is less give to the mortar, the water works out of it, and it becomes stiff and difficult to work with a trowel. Also, when sand is too fine, the mortar is apt to set before the bricks can be placed easily.

In some localities, sand occurs in banks, and in some instances, to a large extent, forms the soil. Under no condition should such sand be used for making mortar unless it is tested and washed. Even then, such sand may be too fine for ordinary mortar. Too much sand in any

Mortar Is Gathered and Troweled in the Shape of a Cigar for Easy Handling
Detroit Building Trades School, Detroit, Michigan

mortar causes the bricklayer to drop considerable mortar off the trowel. This is because the excess of sand robs the mortar of its ability to hang together.

Once mortar has set, it should not be disturbed. If it is disturbed, it will not properly unite and becomes quite useless.

Often smooth-textured face bricks are laid with small or thin bed joints. In order to make mortar which can be spread to make joints as thin as $\frac{1}{8}''$, it is necessary that it be of fine texture. This can be accomplished by using sand which is fine in character. (This is in direct contradiction to foregoing explanations relative to sand and is the only permissible exception to the rule.) Mortar for thin joints should be "fat" and is known as "buttering" mortar.

FROZEN MORTAR. If mortar freezes, it should not be used. The freezing destroys its bonding ability and renders it entirely worthless.

MORTAR COLOR. Color is sometimes added to mortar as a means of making it contrast with the color of the bricks, thus producing a wall of pleasing appearance.

Prepared Mortars. There are many prepared mortars for sale under different trade or manufacturers' names. These can be used successfully providing they are mixed according to the manufacturer's directions and providing they meet standard specifications.

One example of a prepared mortar is the product called *Brixment,* put out by the Louisville Cement Company. This mortar, when used to lay brick or masonry units, is prepared by mixing one bag of Brixment with three cubic feet of damp sand (approximately 240 pounds) followed by the use of sufficient water to give a workable consistency.

Brixment is composed of a blend of natural cement and Portland cement. During manufacture, optimum quantities of waterproofing agents and air-entraining agents are incorporated. Its improved resistance to sulphates is an added attribute contributed by the natural cement it contains.

Natural cement is a very valuable constituent of masonry cement because it has gradual strength-gaining properties combined with high plasticity, excellent water retention, and adheres well with aggregates. As a result, the characteristics of natural cement, combined with the early strength properties of Portland, provide a hydraulic cement that is ideally suited for masonry cement.

Bonding Factors. During the construction period, it is important that all brick be wetted or in a damp condition when used. Bricks vary in water absorption from one gram (20 drops) to 100 grams (½ cupful) of water that is absorbed in one minute. When bricks absorb water at the rate of more than 20 grams a minute, the best bond cannot be expected with any mortar. Under these conditions the mortar will be robbed of water and therefore will not be sufficiently mobile to allow a good contact between brick and mortar.

A good bond of the fine cement particles to the brick surface is possible only when the mortar remains damp enough for a period of time after being placed between bricks. It is especially important to keep bricks wetted when construction goes on during dry weather. This will help provide the conditions necessary for the mortar to harden normally and develop a bond with the brick.

Temperature is also important in controlling the rate of hardening of mortar. With summer temperatures of 90° F., mortar will normally start to harden within an hour. At temperatures of 40° F., the time required for mortar to start hardening may be delayed to twelve hours or longer.

Mortar Types and Materials. For the purpose of discussion mortars may be classified into five general types on the basis of the composition of the cementitious material. These are: straight lime mortars, straight cement mortars, cement-lime mortars, masonry cement mortars, and lime-pozzolana mortars. On the basis of proportions, cement-lime mortars usually are classified in accordance with the ratios of cement to lime, the more commonly used compositions being 1:¼:3, 1:1:6, 1:2:9, and 1:4:15, or types A, B, C, and D, respectively. The figures represent the relative proportions by volume of cement to lime to sand.

The primary components of a mortar are the cementitious material, the aggregate, and water. Each of these serves its particular and essential function and each should be of the best quality available in the locality but within the prescribed cost limits of the job. Masonry should be built for permanence and from this point of view the cost consideration should not be so important that the ultimate goal of a durable structure of pleasing appearance cannot be attained.

After the Mortar Has Been Applied, Brick Are Pressed into Place; the Surplus Mortar
Oozes Out and Then the Joint Is Struck with a Trowel

Detroit Building Trades School, Detroit, Michigan

"Practice" Wall Above Embodies Various Types of Work Done by Brick Masons

This wall displays specimens of good craftsmanship, including the laying of glass blocks. It is not intended to be an example of good design or suitable decorative treatment.

Detroit Building Trades School, Detroit, Michigan

CHAPTER II

Where Bricks Are Used

THEORY OF WALLS AND PARTITIONS

There are several general aspects of theory which should be understood in order that walls and partitions can be selected, designed, and constructed properly. Typical examples are here explained.

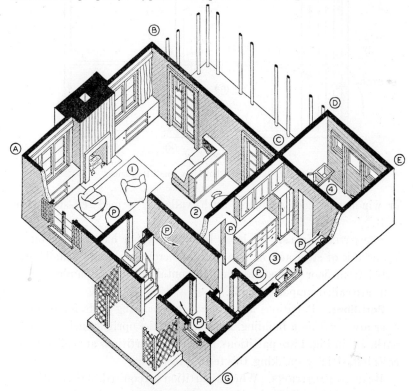

Fig. 1. Cutaway View of a Typical Small Residence

Walls. With regard to residences and other buildings, walls are thought of as the upright enclosing parts of the structure. For example, in Fig. 1, walls are shown at *AB*, *BC*, *CD*, *DE*, *EG*, and *GA*. These walls actually enclose the residence. Sometimes such walls are called *outside walls* but the term *wall* or *walls* is sufficiently descriptive and true of any type of building when used with this definition in mind.

SELF-SUPPORTING WALLS. In residences and other small buildings, masonry walls are not supported by any structural members other than the foundations. Between the foundations and the tops of roof lines of such structures, the walls are continuous or without interruption except

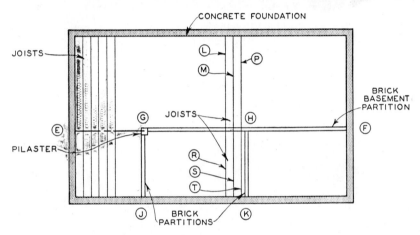

Fig. 2. Basement Plan for a Small Residence

for window or door openings. Such walls are termed self-supporting walls.

SUPPORTED WALLS. In large buildings which have a skeleton or framework of steel and/or reinforced concrete, walls are usually supported from floor to floor by the horizontal beams or spandrels. Such walls are called supported walls.

Partitions. Partitions are the upright enclosing parts for rooms or other areas *within* a building. For example, the upright enclosing parts marked *P* in Fig. 1 are partitions. Sometimes partitions are called *inside walls* but, strictly speaking, this term is incorrect.

BEARING PARTITIONS. When a partition is required to partially support joists, it is called a bearing partition. For example, note partition *GF* in Fig. 2. It can be seen that joists *L*, *M*, and *P* and *R*, *S*, and *T* are supported at one end by the partition. A portion of the floor load which the joists carry is transferred to the partition supporting them. Thus, the partition must support part of the heavy floor loads in addition to its own weight and that of the joists. Bearing partitions are designed primarily to give them sufficient strength to support such loads safely. As these loads may be great, adequate design is essential.

Another example of bearing partitions is shown in Fig. 3 where *AB* and *CD* represent such partitions. Partition *AB* supports one end of the attic joists between *A* and *E*, and *F* and *A* plus part of the attic floor load. Partition *CD* supports one end of the joists between *JB* and *KB*, the second floor load, and the entire load supported by partition *AB*. This situation shows even

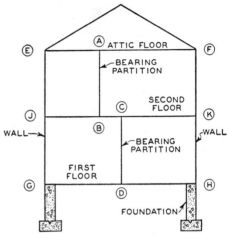

Fig. 3. Sketch Showing a Two-Story Residence in Section

more clearly that bearing partitions must be carefully designed to assure their being strong enough to support the loads.

NONBEARING PARTITIONS. When partitions are used entirely as a means of enclosing a room or other area and do not have to support joists or floor loads, they are called nonbearing partitions. Partitions *GJ* and *HK* in Fig. 2 come under this classification. The design of this type of partition is possible with only a few simple requirements being considered.

Partitions frequently are made thicker than structural requirements demand in order to conceal plumbing pipes, heating ducts, clothes chutes, etc. However, partition thicknesses should always be in multiples of 2, such as 4″ and 6 inches. All openings, as for windows and doors, must have some form of lintel over their tops.

Parapet Walls. Apartment, store, and other such buildings usually have flat or nearly flat roofs. In such structures the walls are built up somewhat higher than the roofs as indicated in Fig. 4.

The stability of the parapet wall is of considerable importance be-

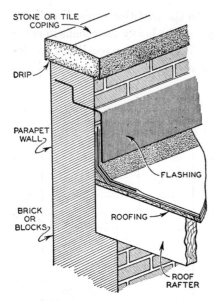

STONE OR TILE COPING

DRIP

PARAPET WALL

BRICK OR BLOCKS

FLASHING

ROOFING

ROOF RAFTER

Fig. 4. Section of a Parapet Wall

cause of the danger to life and surrounding property in the event of damage to it during wind storms or earthquakes. In most cities, building codes rigidly regulate the height of the parapet wall. Such regulations should be carefully followed. In those localities where no building code exists, it is recommended that for walls 8″, 12″, 16″, and 20″ thick, the parapet walls should not be higher than 2′, 3′, 6′, and 9′ respectively. These heights have a safety factor based on wind velocities up to 60 miles an hour. In earthquake regions it is suggested that parapet walls should not be higher than twice their thickness to better resist sudden shock.

Note the flashing recommended for the parapet wall as shown in Fig. 4. Flashing is an important means of preventing roof leaks around the walls.

Wall Copings. Exposed walls such as parapets should be coped or finished similar to the wall shown in Fig. 4. Such copings are made of stone, concrete, tile, and other materials. They can generally be purchased in various widths ready to set on walls of different thicknesses. The basic purpose of coping is to prevent the penetration of water into the joints of the wall. Thus, they are a structural safeguard as well as a means of architectural treatment. The mortar joints between copings and wall tops should be

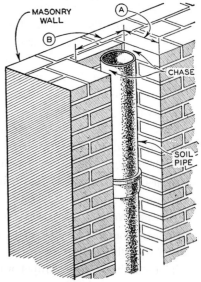

MASONRY WALL

A

B

CHASE

SOIL PIPE

Fig. 5. Chase in a Masonry Wall

carefully made. Also, provisions should be made to allow for expansion and contraction. If coping, as shown in Fig. 4, is not confined by the masonry of the walls, no expansion or contraction damage is likely.

Wall Chases. Chases are square or rectangularly shaped vertical recesses in walls which are provided to accommodate pipes, heating ducts, and similar equipment. The horizontal section of the wall shown in Fig. 5 illustrates a typical chase. In general, chases should not be deeper (dimension A in Fig. 5) than one-third the thickness of the walls they are in. Table I gives recommended chase dimensions for the more commonly encountered pipe sizes. Chases for other purposes than shown in Fig. 5 should be designed by a structural engineer since too large a chase in a wall of a given thickness would seriously weaken the wall.

TABLE I. CHASE DIMENSIONS

PIPE SIZE IN INCHES	DIMENSION A (FIG. 5) IN INCHES	DIMENSION B (FIG. 5) IN INCHES
2	4½	6
3	5½	8
4	6½	9
5	7½	10
6	8½	12

Corbeling of Brick Walls. When brickwork is corbeled out to provide support for various structural members, each succeeding course should not project more than 2″ beyond the course below. The maximum projection of corbeling beyond the face of a wall should not be more than one-half of the wall thickness. Several examples of corbeling are given in Chapter V.

When other structural members are supported by wall corbeling they constitute what engineers call *eccentric loads*. If such loads are especially heavy they have a tendency to affect the stability of the wall. Such walls, therefore, should be designed by a structural engineer. If the services of such an engineer cannot readily be obtained, masons are advised to erect pilasters under such loads rather than run the risk of constructing a wall which would be unstable because of the eccentric loading placed upon it.

Openings in Unit Masonry Walls. Openings such as for doors and windows, in walls built of individual masonry parts (units), should be

Fig. 6. Residence Constructed of Face Bricks

located so as to avoid, as far as is possible, the cutting of any of the units in order to make them fit. For example, suppose a brick wall were to be constructed using standard bricks with ⅜″ mortar joints. A window or door opening in this wall should be located so that whole bricks can be laid between the side of the window or door opening and the nearest corner of the wall.

Fire Resistance of Brick Walls and Partitions. Walls and partitions constructed of brick are perhaps more fire resistant than most other kinds of walls. The resist-ance of various thicknesses is described in the U.S. Bureau of Standards *Letter Circular No. 228.* This letter should be obtained and studied when fire-re-sistive walls or partitions are to be designed and constructed.

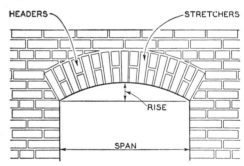

Fig. 7. Typical Segmental Arch in a Brick Wall

Arches in Brick Walls.
In most cases, arches in brick walls are supported by some form of lintel. However, segmental arches of the kind shown in Fig. 7 can be constructed so as to be safely self-supporting. Note the rise which is

indicated in Fig. 7. The rise for such arches should be equal to 1″ for every foot of span. For example, if the span is 4′0″, the rise should be at least 4 inches. Note that standard bricks can be used with alternate headers and stretchers.

Solid Brick Walls. Solid brick walls may be constructed of clay or concrete bricks, either of which give pleasing and strong walls. Clay bricks may be obtained in many surface textures and colors. Concrete

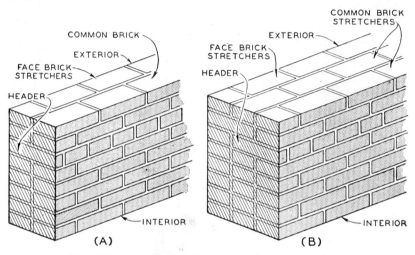

Fig. 8. Eight- and Twelve-Inch Brick Walls in Common Bond

bricks can be used plain or may be painted any desired color. Fig. 6 shows a residence with typical clay brick walls.

Depending upon building code requirements or strengths desired for walls, solid brick walls are made in thicknesses of 4″, 8″, 12″, 16″, etc., all of which are multiples of four inches. Fig. 8 illustrates an 8″ wall at (A) and a 12″ wall at (B). Note that the common bond was used.

Fig. 9 shows section views of the head, jamb, and sill of a window in an 8″ brick wall as well as a section view of the entire wall from footing to roof. Common bond is the pattern which has been used in these sections. Note that the top plate is anchored by ½″ round anchor bolts 10″ long and spaced 8′0″ apart. Notice that joist ends must be beveled where they have their bearing in the wall. The window head section shows that a segmental arch is employed which is similar to that shown in Fig. 7. Such an arch supports only the exterior course of the brick

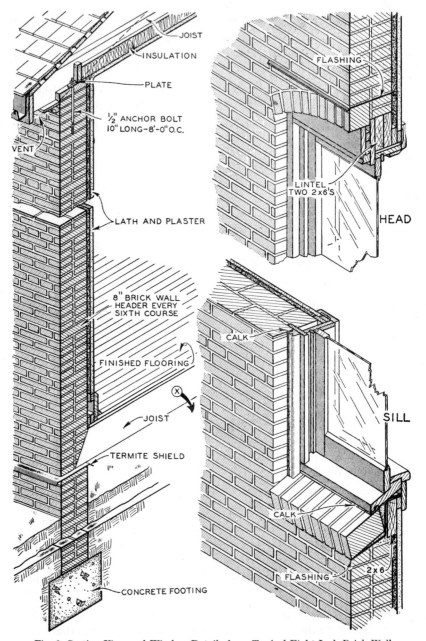

JOIST

INSULATION

PLATE

½" ANCHOR BOLT
10" LONG–8'-0" O.C.

VENT

LATH AND PLASTER

8" BRICK WALL
HEADER EVERY
SIXTH COURSE

FINISHED FLOORING

X

JOIST

TERMITE SHIELD

CONCRETE FOOTING

FLASHING

LINTEL
TWO 2x6'S

HEAD

CALK

SILL

CALK

FLASHING   2x6

Fig. 9. Section View and Window Details for a Typical Eight-Inch Brick Wall

wall. A wood lintel is necessary to support the interior courses. The jamb and sill sections show common construction practice, including brick sills as pictured in Fig. 6.

Brick Partitions. As previously explained, such partitions may be of the bearing or nonbearing type. Their thickness depends upon their type and the requirements expected of them. As for walls, either clay or concrete bricks can be employed in building these partitions.

Fig. 10 shows the commonly used 4″ partition at (A) and a 2¼″ partition at (B). The 4″ partition is frequently employed as a bearing

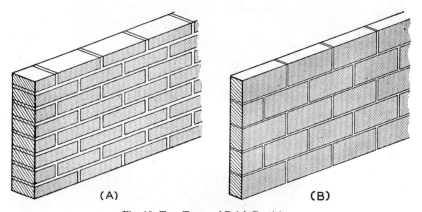

(A)   (B)

Fig. 10. Two Types of Brick Partitions

partition. When properly constructed, using a strong mortar and thin joints, a brick partition of this thickness can safely support heavy loads, especially if pilasters are incorporated into the partition at intervals of not more than ten feet. Some building codes prohibit the use of brick bearing partitions which are less than 8″ in thickness. However, such a restriction is not always justified. The 2¼″ partition should never be used to carry more weight than its own.

The bond recommended for solid brick partitions is illustrated in (A) of Fig. 10. It is known as the *stretcher* bond.

Brick partitions of from 4″ to 8″ in thickness are frequently used to enclose basement spaces as well as to support floor joists. Such partitions are shown in Fig. 2. The pilaster or column at *G* and the intersecting partition at *H* impart ample stability to the long partition *GF*. Such partitions may be used for any enclosure providing footings or

The Mortar Layer in This Bed Joint Is Too Thin
Bed joints should be spread in a thick layer to insure proper bonding.
Louisville Cement Company, Louisville, Kentucky

The Furrow in the Mortar Should Be Shallow, Not Deep
When the furrow is shallow, excess mortar fills the furrow and insures full bed joints.
Louisville Cement Company, Louisville, Kentucky

other ample support is supplied. They should never be used above the basement in a wood-frame building.

The 2¼" partitions are frequently used to enclose closets, rooms, etc., where they need support no weight but their own and where they will not be subject to side forces as are the partitions surrounding a coal storage space or a granary. When such a partition is plastered with ½"

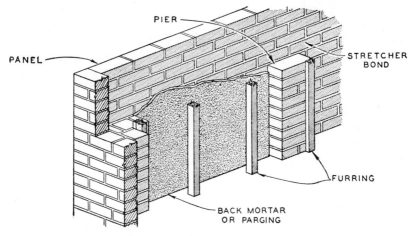

Fig. 11. Pier and Panel Brick Wall

old-fashioned lime plaster on both sides, the carrying of sound through the partition is practically eliminated.

Openings in brick partitions, such as for doors, must have lintels over them. For bearing partitions, steel lintels are recommended. For nonbearing partitions 2 x 4, 4 x 4, etc., wood lintels may be used safely.

Pier and Panel Walls. This kind of wall was developed as a means of saving appreciable amounts of material and labor. For this reason, it is known as an economy wall. A portion of this kind of wall is shown in Fig. 11. Note the panel and piers. The panels are 4" thick, while the piers are at least 8" square. The piers are made integral parts of the panel. Fig. 12 shows a typical wall section and pictorial views of suggested details. Fig. 13 illustrates recommended window details.

The use of pier and panel walls is generally limited to one-story residences and other small, one-story structures. Such walls also can be used as garden or boundary walls.

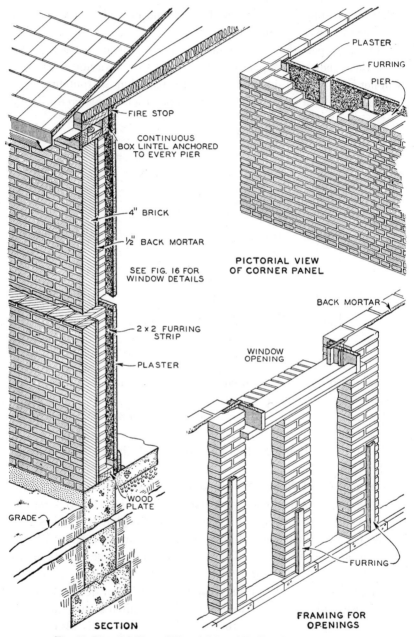

FIRE STOP

CONTINUOUS
BOX LINTEL ANCHORED
TO EVERY PIER

4" BRICK

½" BACK MORTAR

SEE FIG. 16 FOR
WINDOW DETAILS

2 x 2 FURRING
STRIP

PLASTER

WOOD
PLATE

GRADE

SECTION

PLASTER

FURRING

PIER

**PICTORIAL VIEW
OF CORNER PANEL**

BACK MORTAR

WINDOW
OPENING

FURRING

**FRAMING FOR
OPENINGS**

Fig. 12. Pictorial View of Pier and Panel Wall with Typical Details

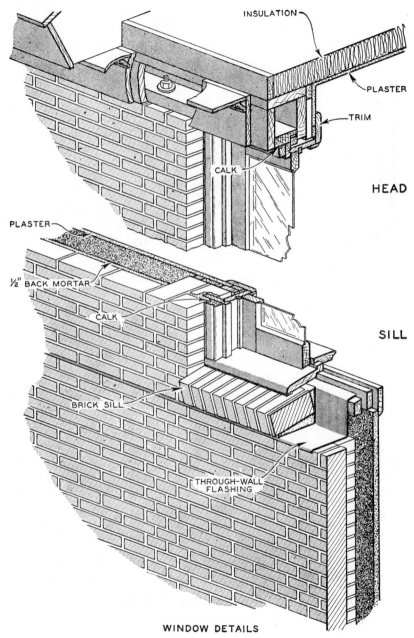

INSULATION

PLASTER

TRIM

CALK

HEAD

PLASTER

½" BACK MORTAR

CALK

SILL

BRICK SILL

THROUGH-WALL FLASHING

WINDOW DETAILS

Fig. 13. Window Details for a One-Story Pier and Panel Wall

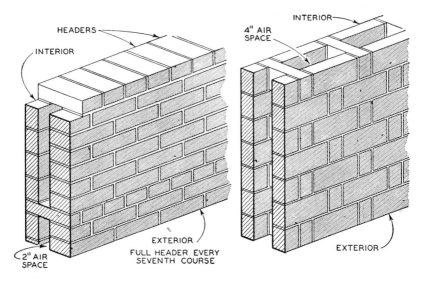

HEADERS

INTERIOR

2" AIR SPACE

EXTERIOR
FULL HEADER EVERY
SEVENTH COURSE

8-INCH ROLOK-BAK WALL

INTERIOR

4" AIR SPACE

EXTERIOR

8-INCH ALL-ROLOK WALL

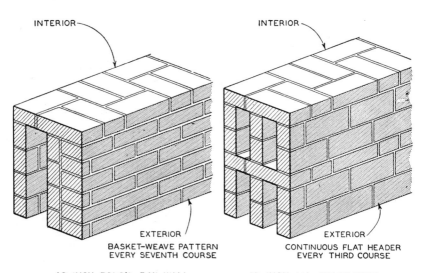

INTERIOR

EXTERIOR
BASKET-WEAVE PATTERN
EVERY SEVENTH COURSE

12-INCH ROLOK-BAK WALL

INTERIOR

EXTERIOR
CONTINUOUS FLAT HEADER
EVERY THIRD COURSE

12-INCH ALL-ROLOK WALL

Fig. 14. Eight- and Twelve-Inch Rolok-Bak and All-Rolok Walls

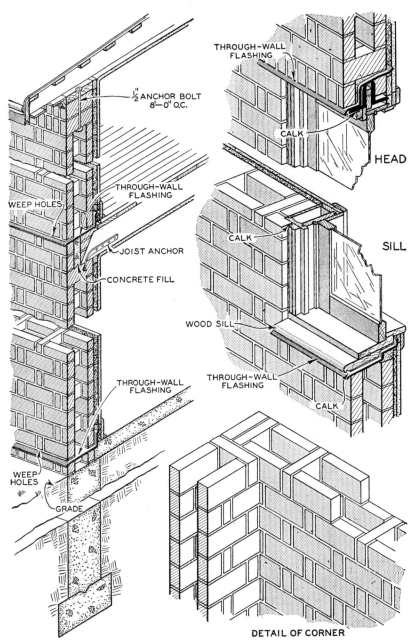

Fig. 15. Pictorial View and Details of Eight-Inch All-Rolok Wall

Rolok-Bak and All-Rolok Walls. Fig. 14 illustrates 8″ and 12″ rolok-bak and all-rolok walls. The rolok-bak wall is a general utility wall. The exterior wythe, or 4″ thickness, is laid with the bricks flat and thus has the appearance of a solid brick wall. The backing wythes are laid with the bricks on edge and a bond between the two is obtained by means of a header course at regular intervals. In all-rolok walls both exterior and interior wythes are laid with bricks on edge with headers two courses apart. The exact difference between 8″ and 12″ rolok-bak and all-rolok walls can easily be seen in Fig. 14. Fig. 15 shows a section and details of a typical 8″ all-rolok brick wall.

Either clay or concrete bricks may be used to advantage in such walls. They are never constructed more than 12″ thick. They may be used for residences, small store buildings, and for various farm structures.

Cavity Walls. Cavity walls are intended to produce a watertight wall which can be plastered direct without the use of furring strips. These walls also tend to enhance thermal and sound insulation. From the exterior they have all the appearances of solid brick walls.

The 2″ cavity between the wythes has the prime purpose of provid-ing a barrier against the passage of moisture and heat or cold to the inner surface of the wall. Cavity walls also can be used to advantage when it is desired that the inside wythe be composed of glazed brick as for laundries, recreation rooms, dairy buildings, etc.

Fig. 16 shows a typical portion of a cavity brick wall. The stretcher type bond is always used. Note that no headers are re-quired since metal ties are employed.

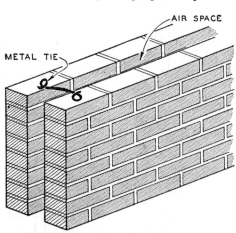

Fig. 16. Cavity Brick Wall

Fig. 17 shows a section and other details of such a wall. Cavity walls can be used wherever an 8″ solid brick wall is used with assurance of at least equal strength.

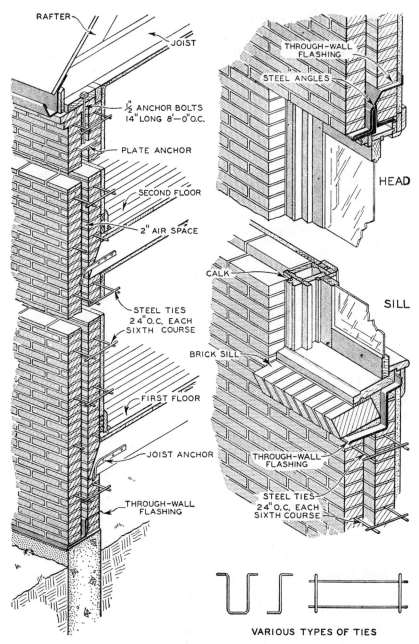

RAFTER

JOIST

½" ANCHOR BOLTS
14" LONG 8'-0" O.C.

PLATE ANCHOR

SECOND FLOOR

2" AIR SPACE

STEEL TIES
2 4" O.C. EACH
SIXTH COURSE

FIRST FLOOR

JOIST ANCHOR

THROUGH-WALL
FLASHING

THROUGH-WALL
FLASHING

STEEL ANGLES

HEAD

CALK

SILL

BRICK SILL

THROUGH-WALL
FLASHING

STEEL TIES
2 4" O.C. EACH
SIXTH COURSE

VARIOUS TYPES OF TIES

Fig. 17. Pictorial View and Details of Ten-Inch Cavity Brick Wall

Brick and Tile. Various combinations of both clay and concrete brick and tile are often used in the construction of walls for residences and other buildings. Such walls have advantages in that they are generally more quickly erected than are solid brick walls and the cells in the tile tend to prevent the passage of moisture, heat, and cold.

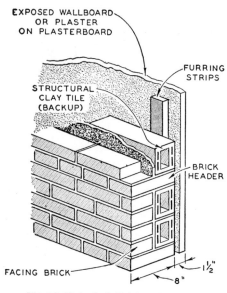

EXPOSED WALLBOARD
OR PLASTER
ON PLASTERBOARD

FURRING
STRIPS

STRUCTURAL
CLAY TILE
(BACKUP)

BRICK
HEADER

FACING BRICK

1½"

8"

Fig. 18. Eight-Inch Brick and Tile Wall

Fig. 18 shows one common manner of using brick and tile in an 8″ wall. This wall has the exterior appearance of a solid brick wall and is strong. Note that brick headers are used every fifth course of exterior brick. The headers serve to bind the wall together.

Fig. 19 illustrates the use of differently shaped tile units in a 12″ brick and tile wall. Note the typical tile units indicated as X and Y and how they are set into the wall. The Y unit provides a space for a brick header every sixth course of exterior brick. In a wall of this kind the plaster can be applied directly to the tile without requiring furring since none of the exterior bricks extend to the inside surface of the wall. Damp-proofing in the form of one heavy coat of asphaltum is recommended as shown in Fig. 19.

Eight and 12″ thicknesses of this kind of wall can be used in the same manner as like thicknesses of solid brick walls. All of the design data explained for solid brick walls applies equally well to this kind of wall. Figs. 18 and 19 show details that are typical.

Brick Veneer Walls. The use of one wythe of brick as a veneer on frame or masonry walls is a means of obtaining the appearance of a solid brick wall plus certain other advantages such as economy in construction and better insulation qualities against the passage through the walls of moisture, and heat and cold.

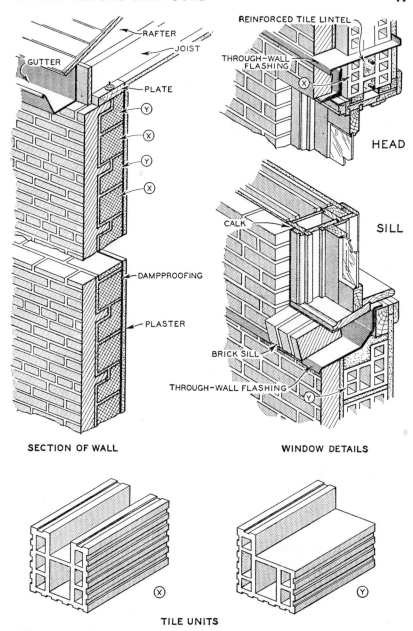

RAFTER

JOIST

GUTTER

PLATE

Ⓨ

Ⓧ

Ⓨ

Ⓧ

REINFORCED TILE LINTEL

THROUGH-WALL FLASHING

Ⓧ

HEAD

DAMPPROOFING

PLASTER

CALK

SILL

BRICK SILL

THROUGH-WALL FLASHING

Ⓨ

SECTION OF WALL

WINDOW DETAILS

Ⓧ

Ⓨ

TILE UNITS

Fig. 19. Pictorial View and Window Details of Twelve-Inch Brick and Tile Wall

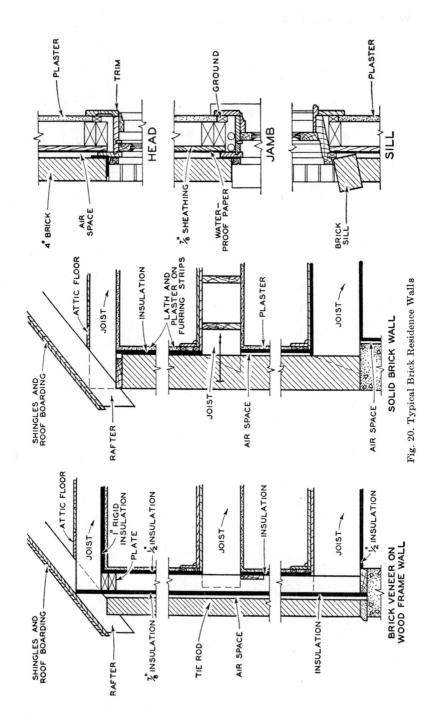

Fig. 20. Typical Brick Residence Walls

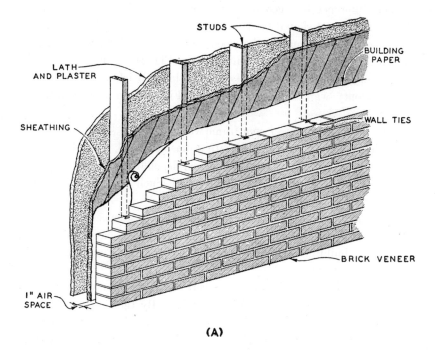

STUDS

BUILDING PAPER

LATH AND PLASTER

SHEATHING

WALL TIES

BRICK VENEER

1" AIR SPACE

(A)

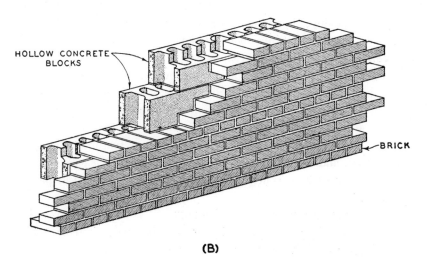

HOLLOW CONCRETE BLOCKS

BRICK

(B)

Fig. 21. Pictorial Views of Brick Veneer on Frame and on Concrete Block Walls

The difference between brick veneer walls and solid walls can be seen in Fig. 20. It should be noted that the brick is simply an addition to the regular structure of the wood frame house. The bricks must be tied to the wood frame as shown in (A) of Fig. 21 and there must be a 1″ air space between them and the sheathing. Brick veneer is placed on a masonry wall as shown in (B) of Fig. 21 and as illustrated in Fig. 18.

Note that brick veneer on a frame wall consists of stretcher bonding throughout, whereas, when used with a masonry wall, it can be bonded by headers every sixth, fifth, etc., course, depending upon the masonry unit used in the principal part of the wall. Such brick may be either clay or concrete.

For the most part, brick veneer is used for residences. In some instances, garages, stores, and other small buildings have such walls. Apartment buildings and other such larger structures must have solid walls.

Brick veneer sometimes serves a very useful purpose when old residences are being remodeled and modernized. By the simple process of adding about 5″ to the outside of the foundation, brick veneer can be constructed over any type of wood frame wall or over any type of masonry wall.

Whenever brick veneer is used, lintels must be put over all window and door openings. For remodeling work, it is recommended that the veneer be started at points about 12″ below the top of the foundation.

Veneered Walls. When brick veneering is used in conjunction with frame buildings, the wood frames carry the necessary loads while the veneering, which is secured laterally by the wood frames, is supported by the foundations. Therefore, the only designing required involves providing a foundation which will be adequate for the support of the veneer, making the selection of color and surface texture of the brick to be used, and deciding upon the joint treatment. If such veneering is bonded into tile or concrete block walls, it is considered as part of the walls.

BRICK VENEER ON OLD FRAME BUILDINGS. As previously suggested, old frame buildings such as residences can be modernized by adding brick veneer to their walls. This is not a difficult task and can be accomplished with little change of the existing walls. The veneering

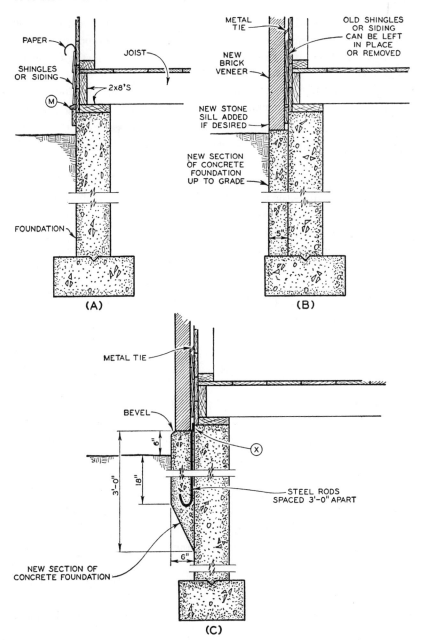

Fig. 22. Typical Methods of Providing Foundations for Brick Veneer over Old Frame Walls

should be supported by the foundation which must, in most cases, be added to the existing foundation. There are several methods of providing the new foundation, three of which are explained in the following paragraphs.

In (A) of Fig. 22 is shown a common type of sill and foundation for a wood frame wall. The drawing at (B) in Fig. 22 illustrates one method of providing a foundation for the brick veneering. Note that the new section of foundation is supported by the old footing and that it extends only slightly above grade. Another method of providing a foundation for brick veneering is shown in (C) of Fig. 22. Note that this method requires the use of steel tie rods which are embedded in the new section of the concrete foundation and fastened to the old by means of expansion bolts at point X. These tie rods make certain the new foundation does not settle, causing the brick veneer to crack.

A third method of supporting the brick veneer is by means of steel shelf angles which are bolted to the foundation. The veneer is then laid directly on the angle. This latter method is the least desirable of the three methods suggested.

Brick veneer should be at least 1″ and not more than 2″ from the shingle or siding surface of the old wall. It may be necessary to remove such projecting pieces of millwork as the watershed shown at M in (A) of Fig. 22.

The veneer must be tied to the old wall by the use of noncorrodible metal ties spaced 16½″ apart vertically and 16″ apart horizontally. Tar paper or some other heavy building paper should be nailed to the old wall surface as the veneer is laid up. The metal wall ties used in brick veneer construction can be seen in (A) of Fig. 21.

Around window openings, the veneer is set as illustrated in the brick veneer window details section shown in Fig. 20. Note, for example, how the new brick sills are set under the wood sills of the window. Steel lintels are necessary to support the veneer over all window and door openings. In some cases new window and door frames must be put in. Carpenters or representatives of lumberyards should be consulted for advice when necessary. At the cornice the veneer is usually continued until it is housed by the rafters and other cornice members.

Solid Brick Walls. The American Standard Building Code Requirements for Masonry and the Federal Housing Authority (FHA) recommend the following thicknesses for solid brick walls. Residential buildings not exceeding 35' in height may have brick walls 8" in thickness. It has been found that a wall of this dimension possesses ample strength under all normal circumstances. Where unusual conditions exist, such as the possibility of exceptionally high winds or earthquakes, 12" walls should be used. The 12" wall is also recommended for two-story and three-story apartment buildings.

One-story single-family dwellings and one-story private garages may be constructed from 6" through-the-wall brick. The 6" exterior load-bearing walls may not exceed 9' in height, except that the walls may be 15' to the peak of the gables. (See Chapter VII.)

In every instance, state and local building codes should be carefully consulted to determine the exact regulations to be observed.

Solid brick walls should be supported at right angles to the wall face at intervals not exceeding 20 times the nominal wall thickness when laid in recommended mortar. Such support is given by chimney structures, corners of buildings, reinforced concrete floors, interior masonry partitions, or by special pilasters. The use of pilasters, except in long store buildings, is seldom required. When pilasters are needed, they should be square in cross section and twice as thick as the walls they stiffen or support.

The top plates upon which rafters and ceiling joists have their bearing should be bolted to the wall by the use of anchor bolts as shown at the top of the wall section in Fig. 9.

Where floor joists have their bearing in brick walls they should be cut as shown in Fig. 9. Each joist should have a bearing of at least 4 inches. Cutting or beveling the ends of the joists is done to prevent harm to the wall in the event of a fire. If for any reason one or more of the joists fail and drop down, they would fall in the direction of the arrow at X in the section view of Fig. 9, without damaging the wall. The bond used depends primarily upon the architectural effect that is desired.

For ordinary brick walls, a mortar mix of 1:1:6 is amply strong and resistive to the passage of water through walls.

Solid Brick Partitions. A 4″ wall is sufficiently strong when adequate lateral support is provided. The same conditions prevail, regarding partition stability and lateral support, as those affecting walls. For an example of brick partition design, refer to Fig. 2. As previously explained, brick partition *GF* supports the ends of joists *L, M, P, R, S,* and *T.* These joists support the first floor as well as the bearing partitions above them. These bearing partitions in turn support the second floor and attic loads. Suppose this partition must support a load of 3,000 pounds per lineal foot. The load per square inch on the partition

is then $\dfrac{3,000}{4 \times 12} = \dfrac{3,000}{48} =$ approximately 63 pounds.

It is known that brick can support many times this load (unit stress) when it acts directly downward as a compressive load. The 4″ partition, therefore, is safe. However, lateral support is absolutely necessary and is provided by the pilaster at *G,* partition *HK,* and the intersection with the foundation at *F.*

It should be remembered that many local building codes do not allow 4″ bearing partitions under any circumstances. Under such restrictions an 8″ partition would have to be used for *GF.*

Nonbearing brick partitions can range in thickness from 2¼″, as in (B) of Fig. 10, up to and including 8 inches. The 2¼″ partition should not be used where heavy fixtures such as sinks must be supported, or where severe bumps might be expected, as in a coal bin. For other than closet enclosures or for short partitions having ideal conditions of lateral support, the 4″ partition is recommended.

All openings in partitions should have reinforced masonry or steel lintels across them. The bond recommended for such walls is shown in (A) and (B) of Fig. 10. The bond shown in (A) of Fig. 8 is recommended for 8″ partitions. A 1:1:6 mortar mix is recommended.

Pier and Panel Economy Brick Walls. This kind of wall is intended primarily for one-story residences and for small garages, gasoline service stations, and other minor buildings in which the walls need not carry heavy loads. In fact, these walls should not be subjected to loads greater than those coming from short span ceiling joists and roof rafters. Most building codes do not allow this kind of wall in other than one-story buildings.

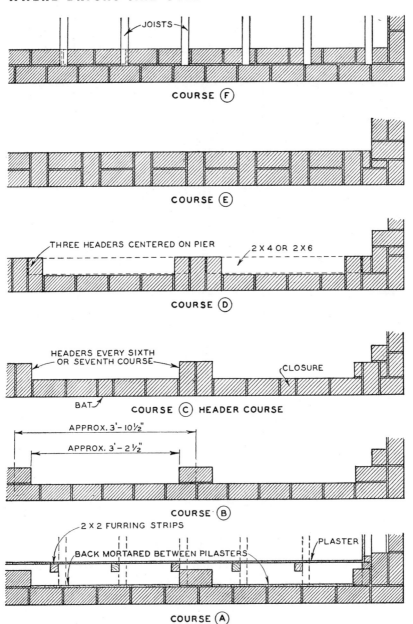

Fig. 23. Plan Showing Construction of Economy Wall by Courses

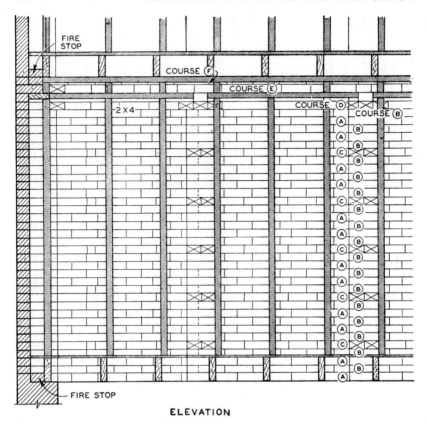

FIRE STOP

COURSE (F)

COURSE (E)

2 X 4

COURSE (D)

COURSE (B)

FIRE STOP

ELEVATION

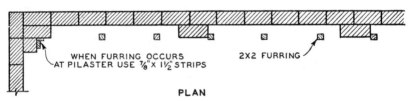

WHEN FURRING OCCURS
AT PILASTER USE ⅞"X I½" STRIPS

2X2 FURRING

PLAN

Fig. 24. Elevation of Economy Wall

Such walls (shown in Figs. 11 and 12) are 4″ thick and are built of brick laid flat in common bond, supported by pilasters 8″ square. Figs. 23 and 24 show the recommended design. Note that the pilasters are approximately 3′10″ from center to center. It is recommended that the inside surface of such walls be plastered with mortar as indicated in course A of Fig. 23.

Fig. 23 gives the recommended design of various courses. Fig. 24

shows these courses in elevation. As shown in Fig. 12, pilasters should be erected against the inside wall on both sides of all window and door openings. From Figs. 23 and 24 it can be seen that 8″ construction is recommended at all sills, girts, and plates. There should be 2 x 2 furring strips between pilasters. Furring strips placed directly on the pilaster should be ⅞″ x 1½″. These strips are shown in the plan view of Fig. 24.

The bonding recommended for such walls is shown in both Fig. 23 and Fig. 24. The mortar for such walls should not be weaker than a 1:1:6 mix.

Rolok Walls. Eight-inch rolok-bak and all-rolok walls such as shown in Figs. 14 and 15 may be used for one- and two-story residences and other small buildings in the same manner as 8″ solid brick walls. Walls of these kinds in 12″ thicknesses may be used the same as 12″ solid brick walls for apartment and other such buildings where only moderate loads must be supported. The use of these kinds of walls for buildings of more than three stories or for buildings where heavy loadings must be supported should not be planned without the assistance of a structural engineer.

Anchors shown in the section view of Fig. 15 should be built into the two top continuous header courses. Joists should also be anchored as shown.

Where joists have their bearing in rolok walls, the bearing surfaces in the walls should be composed of header courses and each joist should have at least 4″ of bearing. Those bonds shown in Figs. 14 and 15 are recommended. Lateral support should be provided, especially for 8″ walls of this kind. A mortar mix of 1:1:4 is recommended.

Brick Cavity Walls. This kind of wall can be used the same as an 8″ brick wall except that the maximum permissible height is only 25 feet. Neither the facing nor the backing in these walls should be less than 3¾″ in nominal thickness, and the cavity should not be less than 2″ nor more than 3″ in width.

As shown in Figs. 16 and 17, the facing and backing should be securely fastened together with steel ties which are coated with some non-corroding protective agent. Note the method of installation for the anchor plate bolts in the section view of Fig. 17.

Joists should have a full 4″ of bearing in the backing tier and should be tied by the use of joist anchors. The bond shown in Figs. 16 and 17 is recommended with a 1:1:4 mortar mix.

BUILDING WALLS AND PARTITIONS

Solid Brick Walls. All solid brick walls must be supported by adequate foundations or footings. Where concrete foundations are used, the concrete should be allowed several days to two weeks for hardening before brickwork is started, depending on whether it was poured in warm or cold weather. If both the walls and the foundation are to be of brick, they can be laid continuously.

The walls are laid up to the level of the first joists. The joists should then be placed and termite shields installed if they are thought necessary. Care should be taken to see that the joist ends are beveled properly, that they are spaced correctly, and that no more than 4″ of bearing surface is allowed. When the joists have been placed, the outside wythe is built up course by course and the interior wythes laid around the joist ends. It will be necessary to cut some bricks in order to make them fit over the beveled ends of the joists.

When building walls which have window and door openings, bricks are laid up on both sides of the openings as shown in Fig. 9. When the jambs have reached the height of the opening, the lintels are carefully set, care being taken to make certain they are laid in mortar. Some of the bricks may have to be chipped slightly in order to make them fit tightly above the lintels. Mortar should be applied to the lintels before setting the first course of bricks on them. The lintels should be placed so that the exterior edge is slightly behind the outside edge of the exterior wythe.

All walls of a building should be laid up at the same level all the way around because of the placement of joists and to provide lateral support. Anchor bolts should be embedded in the joints. If they are too big for the joints, bricks around them are chipped as necessary.

Solid Brick Partitions. Bearing partitions such as *GF* in Fig. 2 must have adequate footings. Nonbearing partitions such as *GJ* and *HK* in Fig. 2 also should have footings. The minimum footing, 12″ wide and 8″ deep, should be ample. Nonbearing partitions should never be set on concrete basement floors as the latter are apt to crack and settle, thus causing the partition to be badly cracked or to fail completely.

Pier and Panel Economy Brick Walls. This kind of brick wall requires a foundation, the thickness of which is somewhat greater than that of the piers. This is shown in the section view of Fig. 12. Figs. 23

and 24 show in detail the manner in which the various courses for this kind of wall are laid. These drawings are self-explanatory. Figs. 12 and 13 show other details which can be used in laying up such walls.

When the panels have been laid, they should be back plastered (back mortar) to a depth of at least ½", using regular mortar.

TABLE II. LENGTHS AND HEIGHTS OF BRICK COURSES LAID WITH 2¼" x 8" BRICK AND ⅜" MORTAR JOINT

NUMBER OF BRICKS	LENGTH OF BRICK COURSES	HEIGHT OF BRICK COURSES
1	8⅜"	2⅝"
2	1' 4¾"	5¼"
3	2' 1⅛"	7⅞"
4	2' 9½"	10½"
5	3' 5⅞"	1' 1⅛"
6	4' 2¼"	1' 3¾"
7	4' 10⅝"	1' 6⅜"
8	5' 7"	1' 9¼"
9	6' 3⅜"	1' 11⅝"
10	6' 11¾"	2' 2¼"
11	7' 8⅛"	2' 4⅞"
12	8' 4½"	2' 7½"
13	9' ⅞"	2' 10⅛"
14	9' 9¼"	3' ¾"
15	10' 5⅝"	3' 3⅜"
16	11' 2"	3' 6"
17	11' 10⅜"	3' 8⅝"
18	12' 6¾"	3' 11¼"
19	13' 3⅛"	4' 1⅞"
20	13' 11½"	4' 4½"
21	14' 7⅞"	4' 7⅛"
22	15' 4¼"	4' 9¾"
23	16' ⅝"	5' ⅜"
24	16' 9"	5' 3"
25	17' 5⅜"	5' 5⅝"

NOTE.—For other than ⅜" joints, calculations can be made to arrive at the lengths and heights of courses. Merely add the thickness of one mortar joint to the length or height of the brick and multiply by the number of bricks in the course.

Rolok Walls. The laying of rolok walls, including window, door, and other details such as foundation requirements, etc., is similar to the laying of other kinds of brick walls.

Cavity Brick Walls. Cavity brick walls are simple to lay in that the brickwork is not complicated and follows the general methods previously explained.

Brick and Tile Walls. Laying up brick and tile walls is done following the same explanations given previously. Figs. 18 and 19 show construction details which are typical of all such walls.

Lengths and Heights of Brick Walls. Table II gives the number of standard bricks (using a ⅜" mortar joint) in courses of various lengths

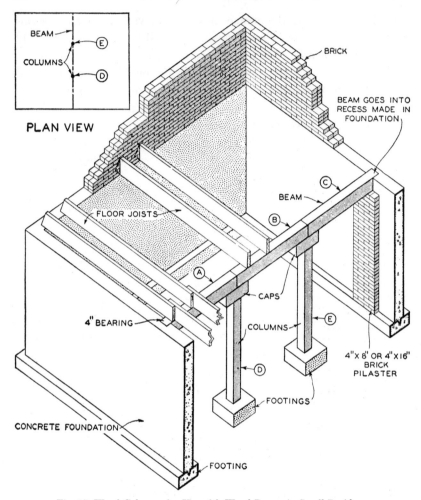

Fig. 25. Wood Columns for Use with Wood Beams in Small Residence

as well as the heights of these courses. This table can be used in planning the sizes and locations of all openings in brick walls so as to avoid the necessity for cutting bricks at the jambs, heads, and sills of doors and windows.

THEORY OF COLUMNS

In practically all cases where beams are used in residences, farm buildings, and other small structures, there must be one or more supporting members for the beams. These supporting members are commonly called posts, pillars, or columns. The term *column* is technically correct and is employed in this text. Architects and engineers generally design the columns in a given structure just as they do the beams. But there are times when a mason must design columns as well as set or build them. Columns, like beams, are of great importance. The safety of an entire structure depends upon them since they are the means of supporting beams. An exception to this statement occurs when one end of a beam is supported by a foundation or side wall or where beams are used to support sections of walls. In such cases the walls directly under the bearing surfaces of the beams act as columns and must be strong enough to carry the loads safely.

The plan and pictorial view of a basement for a small barn, residence, or other building showing the joists, beams, and columns, is shown in Fig. 25. Note that the beam is composed of three parts, *A*, *B*, and *C*, and that it is supported by columns *D* and *E* as well as by the foundation. Part *A* of the beam is supported at one end by the foundation and at the other by column *D*. Part *B* of the beam is supported at its ends by columns *D* and *E*. Part *C* of the beam is supported at one end by column *E* and at the other end by the foundation.

A wood beam must be short in length because it is not strong enough, even in large sizes, to support heavy loads over long spans. It should be emphasized that even if a large wood beam in one piece strong enough to support safely heavy loads over long spans could be obtained, its depth would be so great as to cut down seriously the headroom in the basement. In addition, the cost of such a large wood beam would be prohibitive. For these reasons, beams of shorter lengths are used with columns where necessary, as shown in Fig. 25.

In many cases, one-piece steel I beams could be used which would carry the load safely. Again, the depth of the beam as well as its cost would make its use impractical. The same conditions are true also of reinforced concrete or other types of masonry beams. In order to insure building a safe structure, avoid prohibitive construction costs, and conserve basement headroom, beams of short length must be used in conjunction with columns.

The same reasoning also applies where beams are used to support haymow floors in barns or other floors above the first floor level.

In some cases it is desirable to have partitions in a basement or on the first floor of a building, as, for example, a barn. Such partitions are usually constructed of bricks or concrete blocks and thus are able to serve as supports for one or more beam ends. Fig. 26 shows a small residence basement which has partitions between *G* and *F* and a beam and column between *E* and *G* instead of beams and columns running between *E* and *F*. These provide enclosed space for coal bins, garages,

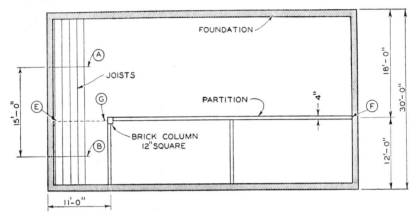

Fig. 26. Basement Partitions, When Required, Are Made of Masonry and Are Used to Support Floor Loads

and other small rooms and, if built of bricks or concrete blocks, take the place of columns and beams. A steel beam would be required between *E* and *G*, however. At *G* the partition would have to be enlarged to form a column because one end of beam *EG* would have to be supported. The regular partition would not be strong enough to support it since it carries a *concentrated load*. This is explained as follows:

The side view of **I** beam *EG* is shown in Fig. 27. This beam spans a distance of 11'0 inches. The end at *E* is supported by the foundation wall while the other end at *G* is supported by the brick column which can be seen in Fig. 26. The arrows above the beam in Fig. 27 represent these joists. In order to make the problem easier to visualize, the first floor live and dead load will be assumed as 60 pounds per square foot, the weight resulting from first floor partitions not being taken into consideration. The length of the floor area between lines *A* and *B* is 15'0" while the width is 11'0 inches. If the combined live and dead load is

60 pounds per square foot and the area of the floor 165 square feet
(15'0" × 11'0"), the total floor load will be 165 × 60, or 9,900 pounds.
Thus, the beam in Fig. 27 supports 9,900 of an *equally distributed load*.
The load is said to be equally distributed because each joist along the
beam has an equal load. For this reason, along every foot of the beam
the load is equally distributed.

A beam with an equally distributed load and supported at its ends
as shown in Fig. 27 in turn distributes half its load to each support. In

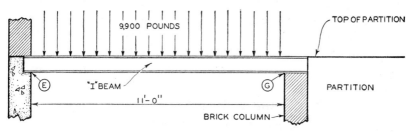

Fig. 27. Beam *EG* Shown in Fig. 26

other words, in Fig. 27, half of 9,900, or 4,950 pounds, is supported by
the foundation and 4,950 pounds by the brick column. Each of these
4,950 pound loads is a concentrated load so far as the foundation and
brick column are concerned because the beam causes the loads to fall at
one spot on the brick column and at one spot on the foundation wall. If
the second floor and attic floor loads plus the loads resulting from the
weight of partitions were added to the 9,900 pounds, the total weight
beam *EG* would have to carry would probably be more than three times
as great, or in the neighborhood of 32,000 pounds. In that event, each
concentrated load would be about 16,000 pounds.

When uniformly distributed loads are carried, brick partitions such
as those between *G* and *F* in Fig. 26 might possibly be as thin as four
inches. Brick partitions are explained in greater detail in succeeding
pages. However, a 4" wall alone under the beam end at *G* would not
be strong enough to support the concentrated load of 16,000 pounds.
Therefore, the partition directly under the beam end bearing point is
increased in size to the extent that the column thus formed is 12"
square.

In most cases the concrete foundation will be capable of safely
supporting such a concentrated load. If the load is considered too great

or if there is any doubt at all of the foundation's ability to support the load, a pilaster 4″ thick and 12″ wide is constructed.

KINDS OF COLUMNS

There are many kinds of columns. They differ according to the materials from which they are made and the various uses to which they are put. It will be found that very few exact recommendations are made as to the kinds of columns to use in specific places. This is due to the many varying factors relative to allowable costs, availability, and geographical locations. Generally speaking, the individual making the selection of columns chooses those types which he feels will serve the purpose to the best advantage. Each situation should be studied carefully and the type of column selected which best meets the conditions encountered.

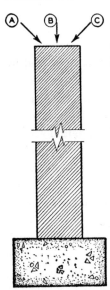

Fig. 28. Application of Loads to a Brick Column

Brick Columns. Brick columns are seldom used unless the basement partitions or foundations are constructed of bricks. One use for the brick column has already been explained in the description of the enlarged section of the brick partition at *G* in Fig. 26. This column supports one end of the beam which spans the distance between *E* and *G*.

Where beam ends are supported by concrete foundations, brick pilasters are frequently built as shown in Fig. 25. The purpose of the pilaster is, of course, to help support part of the load from the beam end, particularly if the foundation wall is only 8″ in thickness. An 8″ foundation will allow only 4″ of bearing surface for beam ends. The size of such pilasters depends on the load from the beam and on the amount of bearing surface available for the beam in the foundation.

Brick columns, even when they are built without steel reinforcing bars,[2] have a great deal of what engineers call *compressive strength*. In simple terms this means that a brick column can support a great load safely as long as that load is ap-

---

[2] For additional material on reinforced brick masonry, see *Brick Engineering* by Plummer and Reardon, published by the Structural Clay Products Institute.

plied straight down and not from one side. For example, note Fig. 28 in which arrows *A, B,* and *C* represent loads being applied to a brick column. If the load applied is straight down as indicated by arrow *B,* it will be safely supported if the column is designed and built as will be presently described. However, if there is a tendency for the loads to be applied from either side, as shown by arrows *A* and *C,* a strain is induced which engineers call *bending.* Bending can cause a brick column to fail, so is an important consideration when planning brick columns.

In theory, beams supported by brick columns such as that shown in Fig. 26 across *EG,* transmit their loads straight downward. However, one or more imperfections in the structural work of a building might easily cause the load supported by the column to be applied other than straight down. To avoid any possibility of bending in the column, it is made larger than seems necessary at the time of its design.

If a brick column is part of a brick partition, as in Fig. 26, the partition will have a tendency to strengthen the column against bending. However, it is best to design the column as though it had been intended to stand alone.

When columns receive the loads of beams, their dimensions should be sufficient so that their compressive strength per square inch is not exceeded. Formula (1) is used to determine the required dimensions.

$$Formula\ (1) \qquad\qquad A = \frac{P}{f}$$

A = required area of brick column in square inches
P = load
f = allowable compressive working stress in pounds per square inch

As a means of understanding the application of this formula, it will be assumed that beam *EG* in Fig. 26 supports 32,000 pounds. The problem will be to determine the size of column *G* in square inches.

The column supports only half of the beam load or 16,000 pounds since it is an equally distributed load. The City of Chicago building code allows an *f* value of 200 pounds per square inch when hard-burned bricks and Portland cement mortar are used.

Using formula (1), the first step is to substitute values for the various letters. A trial value for *A* is selected which, in this first example, is

64 square inches or the area of an 8″ x 8″ column. The value of P is 16,000 pounds. The value of f is 200 pounds. Then:

$$64 = \frac{16,000}{200}$$

$$64 = 80$$

This shows that the 8″ x 8″ column is not large enough because area A has to be at least equal to the 80. Using 144 square inches, or a 12″ x 12″ column, gives:

$$144 = 80$$

The 144 square inch area is greater than the 80 so a 12″ x 12″ column is actually stronger than necessary. This additional strength will increase the resistance to bending. The column will have a satisfactory safety factor and is the one which should be selected for the job. In the case of column G in Fig. 26, the brick partitions on either side of the column will further increase the column's resistance to bending, all of which makes for good design.

If brick columns are used in cases such as illustrated in Fig. 25, the design is developed just as was explained for the preceding problem.

Brick pilasters are used in order to provide increased bearing surface for heavy beam ends and must be designed to share whatever part of the beam load is thought necessary. If the beam at C in Fig. 25 supports a load of 18,000 pounds, half of this load or 9,000 pounds will be transmitted to the foundation. A pilaster normally would be expected to carry half of this load, or 4,500 pounds. The process is as follows:

A trial size for the pilaster is selected first. If the dimensions of this pilaster are 4″ x 8″, the value of A is 4 × 8, or 32 square inches. Substituting values for the various letters in formula (1) it is seen that P is 4,500 and f is 200.

$$32 = \frac{4,500}{200}$$

$$32 = \text{approximately } 23$$

Thus, the 4″ x 8″ brick pilaster is stronger than is actually necessary and will be adequate to handle the job.

A further precaution in the design and erection of brick columns is the strict observance of the height-diameter relationship. The height of

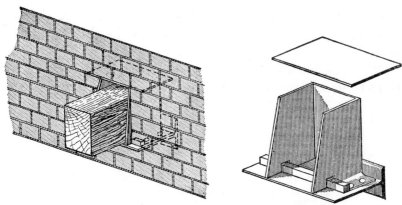

Fig. 29. Method of Supporting Wood Beam in a Brick Wall

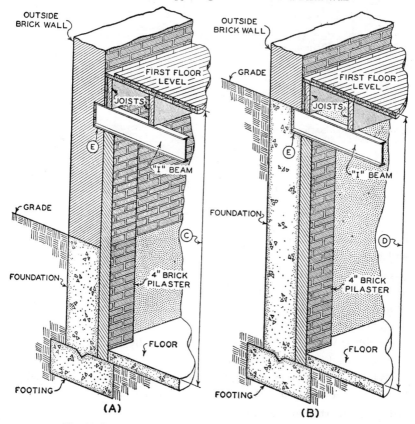

Fig. 30. Beam Support in Brick Wall and Concrete Foundation

a brick column should never be greater than ten times its least dimension. In other words, a 12″ x 12″ column should not be over 10′0″ in height.

When brick columns are to support wood beams, some means must be found to secure them in place. One method is to build anchor bolts

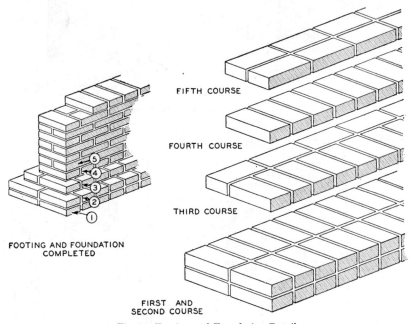

FIFTH COURSE

FOURTH COURSE

THIRD COURSE

FOOTING AND FOUNDATION
COMPLETED

FIRST AND
SECOND COURSE

Fig. 31. Footing and Foundation Details

into the masonry work, leaving enough of the bolt extending so that it will go through a hole in the beam and allow a washer and nut to be screwed on. An alternate method is to provide a channel about two inches in depth at the top of the column into which the beams could fit and be held in place.

When steel beams are to be supported, a steel or wrought iron plate is provided. Where wood beams are supported by a brick wall, a steel wall box (see Fig. 29) is often used.

When brick columns instead of Lally columns are used to support I beams, a steel plate or short section of the I beam should be embedded in mortar at the top of the column as a means of obtaining better distribution of the load throughout the column. The beam ends should be securely bolted to the steel plate or I beam auxiliary bearing surface. (See Fig. 30.)

Brick Footings. Brick masonry has been used successfully for many years as footings for structures of various sizes and types. Since brick is unaffected by alkali or acid, it may be used in any soil. Brick footings should always start with a double course at the base. For ordinary loads, offsets may be made in each course as it is laid. Heavier loads require that the offsets or corbeling be made in every second course, the lower course of each being laid in stretcher bond, the upper in header.

Footing and Foundation Details. Fig. 31 shows how the bricks for a footing and foundation can be bonded to provide strength and durability. The use of ample mortar to assure full mortar joints is important so that the pressure in the foundation and on the footing will be equalized. Use of a mortar made with Portland cement, lime, and sand is recommended for brickwork which is below the surface of the ground. If the soil is wet, the exterior surface of the footing and foundation can be plastered with regular mortar to a depth of ½″ or ¾″ as a means of further waterproofing.

Brick Foundations. There are no generally accepted rules relative to the design of brick foundations as there are for foundations built of concrete. However, the strengths of brick foundations can be calculated by assuming that brickwork, when laid up with Portland cement mortar, has a compressive strength of 200 pounds per square inch. For example, if a brick wall is 8″ wide, its area per lineal foot is 8″ × 12″, or 96 square inches. The strength of such a wall per lineal foot will be 96 × 200, or 19,200 pounds. Because of the great compressive strength of brick, foundations built of them are much stronger than necessary in the majority of cases.

Brick foundations must always be at least as thick as the walls they support and thicker if the load requirements so indicate. A typical brick footing and foundation are shown in Fig. 32. Brick foundations may be laid as soon as the brick footings have been completed. The foundation is started by applying a cement mortar (1:3 mix) to the top of the footing at the corners. Chalk lines or cords are set across batter boards in the marks indicating the face of the foundation. The layout should be carefully checked to avoid errors.

The corners (intersections of side and end building lines) are projected to lower levels by means of a plumb bob. The corners are then laid up to a convenient height (about two or three feet). The use of $\frac{1}{4}''$ vertical and horizontal mortar joints is recommended. Bricks are stepped up from the bottom row toward the corners to permit the proper bonding of the intermediate sections. After two corners have

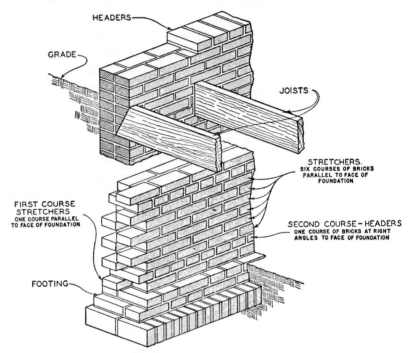

HEADERS

GRADE

JOISTS

STRETCHERS.
SIX COURSES OF BRICKS
PARALLEL TO FACE OF
FOUNDATION

FIRST COURSE
STRETCHERS
ONE COURSE PARALLEL
TO FACE OF FOUNDATION

SECOND COURSE – HEADERS
ONE COURSE OF BRICKS AT RIGHT
ANGLES TO FACE OF FOUNDATION

FOOTING

Fig. 32. Section of Brick Foundation and Footing

been built level and plumb to the desired height, a cord is fastened to hooks or nails which have been driven into the mortar joints at the top of the first course of bricks in each corner. This cord marks the top and outer edge of the first course to be laid between the two built-up corners. Using this line as a guide, the bricks are laid on the footing in a full bed of mortar. To make certain that the bottom of the vertical joints will be filled, mortar is placed on the sides of the brick that will butt against the bricks in place. The brick is then worked into position by shoving, which squeezes the mortar into the joints. The line is moved up one course every time a course of brick has been completed.

When units are cut for the placing of anchor bolts, all voids should be filled with mortar.

The recommended courses for brick foundations are shown in Fig. 32. The first course (stretchers) should be parallel to the face of the wall. The next course (headers) should be at right angles to the face of the wall. The next six courses should be parallel to the face of the wall or stretcher courses. From this point on, one course of headers should be alternated with six courses of stretchers. The spirit level or plumb rule should be used frequently to make certain that the foundation wall is perfectly vertical.

When the mortar has become quite stiff, the joints should be pointed with a small trowel. For foundations below grade level, the pointing can be done by passing the trowel along the joint, pressing the mortar into the joint flush with the outside edge of the bricks.

A well-built brick foundation compares favorably with foundations made of other materials in strength, dependability, and time consumed during construction. The fact that poured-in-place concrete foundations are more common simply means that they can be built using a smaller percentage of skilled labor than is possible when laying up a good brick foundation.

In order to withstand the dampness and chemical properties of the soil, brick foundations should be built of hard-burned bricks and Portland cement mortar.

Mortar Should Be Soft and Plastic When Brick Are Bedded, To Insure
a Good Bond Above as Well as Below the Bed Joint
Louisville Cement Company, Louisville, Kentucky

Mortar Should Have High Water-Retaining Capacity, To Keep Brick
from Sucking Water Out of the Mortar Too Fast
Louisville Cement Company, Louisville, Kentucky

CHAPTER III

Typical Brick Masonry Details

Some typical brick masonry details which will help the reader to visualize construction procedures are illustrated and briefly discussed in the following paragraphs.

Bond Details. A few typical bond details showing how bricks are laid up in courses, are set forth in the following descriptions.

COMMON BOND. Details of this bond are shown in the how-to-lay-brick section, Chapter IV.

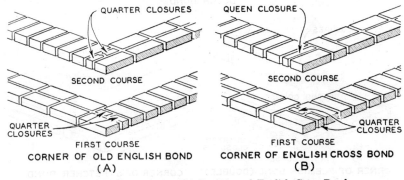

Fig. 1. Bond Details for Old English and English Cross Bond

OLD ENGLISH BOND. In (A) of Fig. 1 is shown the first and second courses of this bond. Note that quarter closures are used in alternate courses on either side of the corner. This is the same bond as illustrated in (D) of Fig. 3, Chapter I.

ENGLISH CROSS BOND. In (B) of Fig. 1 is shown the first and second courses of this bond. Note that this bond differs only slightly from Old English Bond.

DUTCH BOND. In (A) of Fig. 2 is shown a built-up corner of this bond consisting of two courses. Note that half and three-quarter closures are used at the corners. This is the same bond as illustrated in (A) of Fig. 4, Chapter I.

FLEMISH BOND (DOUBLE). In (B) of Fig. 2 is shown the first and second courses of this bond. Note that quarter closures are used near the corners. This is the same bond as illustrated in (B) of Fig. 4, Chapter I.

STRETCHER BOND. In (C) of Fig. 2 is shown two courses for a corner of this bond. This is the same bond as illustrated in (A) of Fig. 3, Chapter I.

Brick Veneer Details. Fig. 3 illustrates typical brick veneer on a wood-framed and sheathed wall. Note that the stretcher-bonded brick

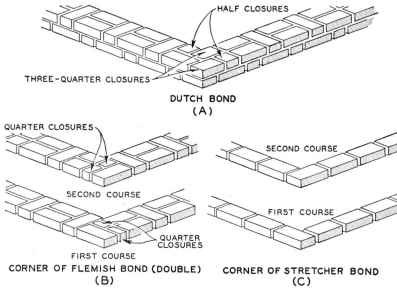

HALF CLOSURES

THREE-QUARTER CLOSURES

DUTCH BOND
(A)

QUARTER CLOSURES

SECOND COURSE

SECOND COURSE

FIRST COURSE

QUARTER CLOSURES

FIRST COURSE

CORNER OF FLEMISH BOND (DOUBLE)
(B)

CORNER OF STRETCHER BOND
(C)

Fig. 2. Bond Details for Dutch, Stretcher, and Flemish Bond

veneer is supported by the concrete foundation. Note, too, the soldier and rowlock courses at the foundation level and window sill. The metal ties are generally spaced two or three bricks apart horizontally and in every fourth or fifth course. There is a space between the paper-covered sheathing and the inside surface of the bricks. This illustration also shows how bricks are laid about the window jambs and sill.

Window and Door Details. (A) and (B) of Fig. 4 show window and door details in brick walls. Note how the bonding is carried out around the window and door and how wood bricks are employed to secure the door frame.

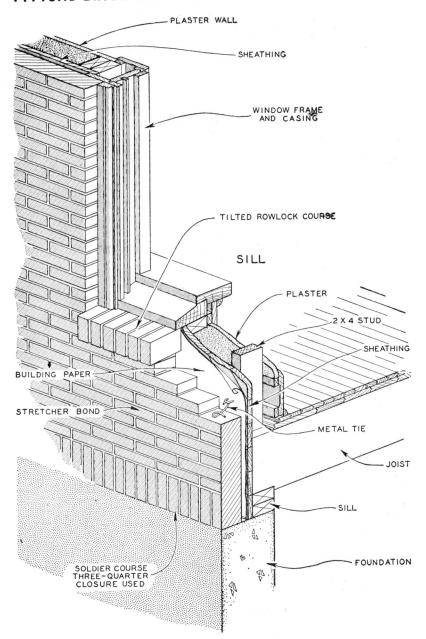

PLASTER WALL

SHEATHING

WINDOW FRAME AND CASING

TILTED ROWLOCK COURSE

SILL

PLASTER

2 X 4 STUD

SHEATHING

BUILDING PAPER

STRETCHER BOND

METAL TIE

JOIST

SILL

SOLDIER COURSE THREE-QUARTER CLOSURE USED

FOUNDATION

Fig. 3. Typical Brick Veneer on Frame

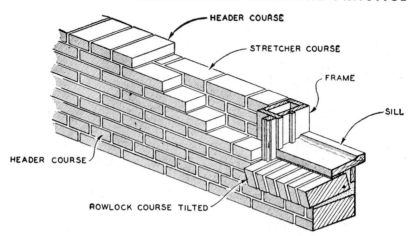

WINDOW FRAME IN BRICK WALL
(A)

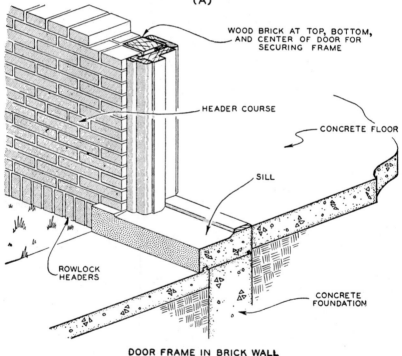

DOOR FRAME IN BRICK WALL
(B)

Fig. 4. Window and Door Details

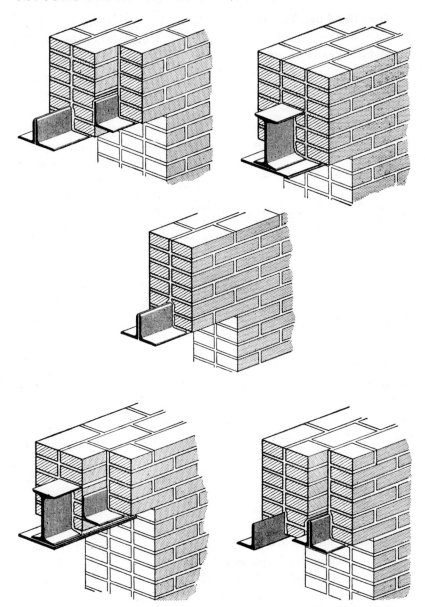

Fig. 5. Manner of Laying Brick around Steel Lintels

Steel Lintel Details. When steel lintels in the forms of angle irons, etc., are used over window and door openings, the bricks must be fitted around them carefully so as to maintain the bond and good appearance. Note in Fig. 5 that bricks are cut so as to fit snugly around the steel members. Plenty of mortar should be thrown on and around the steel as the bricks are laid around it.

Corbeling Details. In many instances walls are corbeled out, that is, enlarged as a means of carrying some extra load or supporting an-

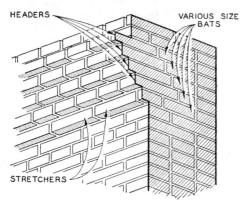

Fig. 6. Typical Corbeling

other structural member. Sometimes the corbeling is entirely a means of adding pattern or beauty to a wall. Chimneys are frequently corbeled to increase their wall thicknesses where they are exposed to the weather.

Fig. 6 shows the details of typical wall corbeling. Note that headers are used to a great extent and that in order to give the corbeling strength, these headers extend into the wall farther than they project beyond it. The first continuous projecting course can be stretchers but all other projecting courses should not extend beyond the under courses more than 2″ and the total projection of the corbeling should not extend more than the thickness of the wall.

Extreme care must be taken in corbeling to see that all joints are completely filled with mortar and that all bricks are level and plumb. The various bats should be cut carefully and fitted into their places.

Grounds Details. When wooden or metal trim or other details are to be secured to brick walls, some means must be provided for fastening them. To accomplish this, pieces of wood take the place of one or more bricks. Note the wood bricks to which is secured the door frame in the illustration in (B) of Fig. 4. This is a typical grounds detail.

Flashing Details. Fig. 7 illustrates typical flashing details for windows and a parapet wall. The use of copper for flashing is recommended. The raggle shown in the parapet wall is a masonry unit which can be purchased ready to lay in the wall.

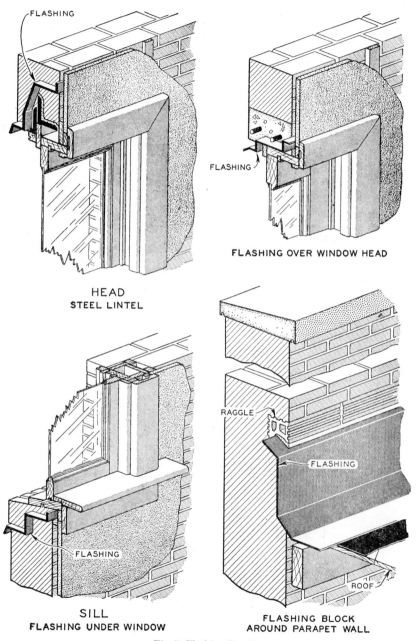

FLASHING

FLASHING

FLASHING OVER WINDOW HEAD

HEAD
STEEL LINTEL

RAGGLE

FLASHING

FLASHING

ROOF

SILL
FLASHING UNDER WINDOW

**FLASHING BLOCK
AROUND PARAPET WALL**

Fig. 7. Flashing Details

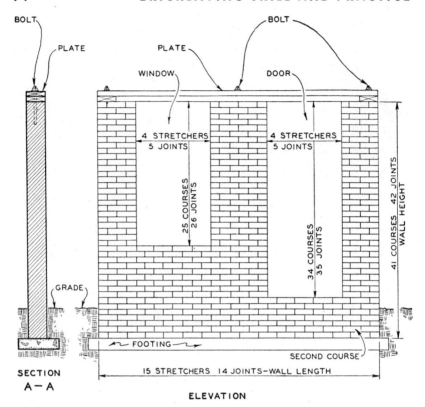

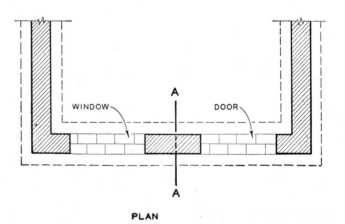

Fig. 8. Lengths and Heights of Brick Courses

Lengths and Heights of Brick Courses. The lengths and heights of all walls and the widths and heights of all window and door openings in the walls should be carefully planned in order that whatever brickwork bond is used, all courses and tiers can be laid without having to use other than whole bricks in the facing tier. Fig. 8 shows an example of this.

The length and height of the wall is such that it contains exactly 15 stretchers and 41 courses. If the length of the wall had been planned a few inches longer or shorter, it would have been necessary for one stretcher to be cut, causing the bricklayer trouble and marring the appearance of the wall. An inch difference in the height of the wall would have made it necessary to make the last course out of bats.

The window and door location and sizes were planned to avoid the use of small closures. Windows and doors can be purchased in many standard sizes which makes possible exact planning.

Planning the length of a wall can be done once the bond has been decided upon. For example, the stretcher bond in Fig. 8 requires all stretcher courses except where headers are necessary around the corners and openings. However, a complete stretcher course, such as the second course shown in Fig. 8, can be used for the planning. Add the width of one mortar joint to the length of one stretcher. This is one unit. The length of the wall can then be made so many units long minus the width of one joint. When planning the height of a wall, add the width of one mortar joint to the height of one brick. The height of the wall can then be made any number of times that amount, minus the thickness of one joint.

Careful planning of all lengths and heights saves the bricklayer trouble and assures a good appearance of the facing tier.

Wall Top Details. The tops of exposed parapet and fire walls should be protected by a coping of some sort to keep water from running down in the joints between bricks. Such copings can be made of tile, stone, concrete, or other impervious materials.

THEORY OF LINTELS

When the outside walls of houses, barns, and other structures are built of masonry veneer or of solid masonry, there must be members resembling beams for the purpose of supporting the masonry work over

The Furrow in This Bed Joint Is Too Deep
A deep furrow may cause an inefficient bond and the danger of water seepage.
Louisville Cement Company, Louisville, Kentucky

Mortar Should Be Spread over a Few Bricks Only
If mortar is spread too far, it will dry out before the next course is applied.
Louisville Cement Company, Louisville, Kentucky

the openings for windows and doors. Occasionally, the masonry work over such openings is made to support itself through forming an arch, but generally, a level window or door head is desired.

Fig. 9 shows an opening in a brick wall which could be for either a window or a door. In this typical example, support is needed for the brickwork over the opening between *AC*. Supports or beams used for such purposes are called lintels.

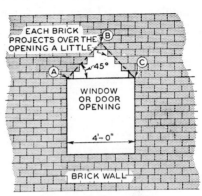

Fig. 9. Window or Door Opening in a Brick Wall and Spandrel

Contrary to what might be expected, the lintel for a lone window in a brick wall must support relatively little of the brickwork directly above the window opening. Actually, only that portion of the brickwork within the isosceles triangle *ABC* requires support. This is explained as follows: If brickwork or any other kind of masonry used in walls is well laid and carefully bonded with a good mortar and thin joints, it will have what is known as a corbeling property. As can be seen in Fig. 9, each brick, starting from the corners of the opening, projects over the opening slightly and tends to carry the upper wall. This means that each brick or other masonry unit will act as a cantilever, supporting the brickwork above it with its projection portion. The overlapping bricks on the two sides of the opening gradually approach each other from course to course until they meet in a point over the center of the opening. Consequently, only the brick inside the triangle *ABC* needs to be supported by a lintel.

When more than one window or door opening occurs in a masonry wall, the lintels over such openings are required to support more of the masonry work. Again using a brick wall as an example, note that window opening *2* is directly over door opening *1* in Fig. 10. In a situation like this, the lintel over the door opening must support all of the brickwork in the area *CDAB*. This is because the corbeling effect just described does not exist where masonry walls are broken by two or more large openings. In other words, the lintel over the door opening must support not only the triangular area discussed in Fig. 20 but the balance of the area as well. This area is known technically as a *spandrel*. Windows *3*, *4*, and *5* present another common condition. In this example, the lintel over window opening *5* must support the column of brickwork *GHEF* plus the areas of brickwork marked *LMJE* and

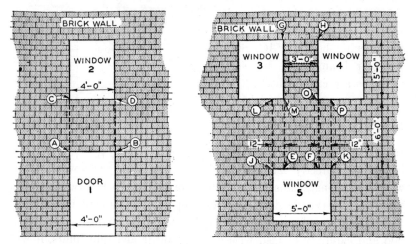

Fig. 10. Various Combinations of Window and Door Openings in a Brick Wall

OPFK. Regarding column *GHEF*, it is safe to assume that above line *GH* the corbeling effect of the brickwork will support the wall without any help from the lintel over window *5*.

There is still another common condition concerning lintels over window and door openings which must be considered. Fig. 11 shows a section and elevation plan of a brick wall between its footing and a point just above the second floor window. The door opening is below the place in the wall where the second floor joists are supported. This means that the lintel over the door opening must support not only the area marked *CDAB* but the loads from the joists *E, F, G,* and *H* as well. This condition pertaining to joist loads occurs in only two sides of a building where wood or steel joists are employed because the joists run parallel to the other two sides of the building. If concrete floors are used, floor loads must be included in the calculations for openings on all sides of the building because such a floor is supported by all four walls.

When lintels are being selected for top-story window openings, it must be remembered that attic floor joists and roof loads must be considered as was just explained for second floor joists. The same conditions apply because where wood or steel joists are used, they are sup-

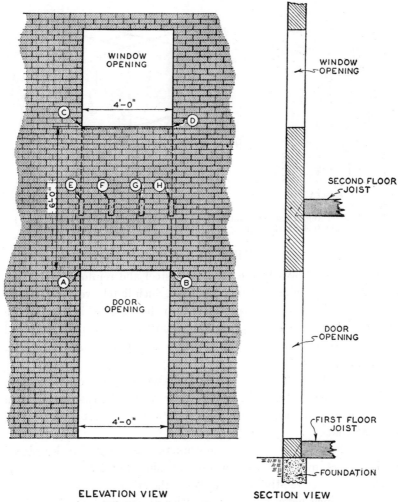

ELEVATION VIEW   SECTION VIEW

Fig. 11. Example of Brick Wall Where Door Opening Lintel Must Support
Second Floor Load in Addition to Spandrel

ported by only two walls of the house. The same situation exists for flat roofs where rafters are used.

Every window, door, or any other kind of opening in a wall built of individual masonry units must have a lintel over it. The support and load conditions for these lintels can be determined if the foregoing explanations are kept in mind.

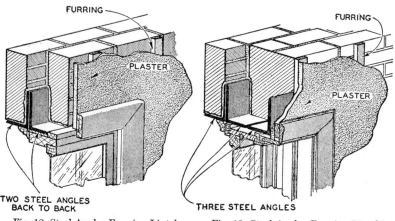

FURRING

PLASTER

FURRING

PLASTER

TWO STEEL ANGLES
BACK TO BACK

THREE STEEL ANGLES

Fig. 12. Steel Angles Forming Lintel
in Eight-Inch Brick Wall

Fig. 13. Steel Angles Forming Lintel in
Twelve-Inch Brick Wall

KINDS OF LINTELS

In the early days before the use of steel and reinforced concrete, masons used heavy oak timbers as lintels. Such lintels were never fully satisfactory because they were subject to shrinkage which caused the masonry they supported to crack. In modern construction, steel and reinforced concrete are used for lintels and only occasionally is wood used.

Steel Angles. Steel angles of various sizes are used for lintels more than any other materials. They are easy to handle, easy to lay, and allow the surrounding masonry to be laid with less trouble than lintels of other kinds.

In 8″ brick walls it is common practice to use two angles placed back to back over a window or door opening. Fig. 12 shows how the angles are placed relative to the wall and the other units of the opening. If angles which have legs of unequal length are used, the longest leg is generally placed in the vertical position because the angle is stronger when set in that manner.

In walls greater than 8″ in thickness, more than two angles can be used. Fig. 13 illustrates a typical arrangement of the use of three angles.

For apartment buildings, some farm structures, and other small buildings having 8″ brick walls, some builders prefer to make up lintels using one steel angle along with a 4 x 6 wooden beam such as shown in Fig. 14. This scheme has some advantages so far as carpentry work is concerned. Such a combination generally forms a satisfactory lintel

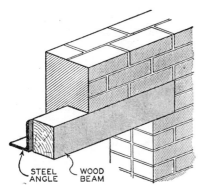
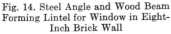

Fig. 14. Steel Angle and Wood Beam Forming Lintel for Window in Eight-Inch Brick Wall

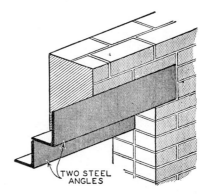

Fig. 15. Steel Angles Forming Lintel for Casement Window in Eight-Inch Brick Wall

where the amount of masonry to be supported is not great and where no joist loads must be considered. Sometimes three 2 x 4's are nailed together to form a 4 x 6 beam. However, the solid 4 x 6 wood beam is best.

Fig. 15 shows the details of another way in which two steel angles can be used as a lintel over a casement window in an 8″ brick wall.

In a brick veneer wall such as shown in Fig. 16, the wood frame section of the wall over the opening is amply supported by the header which in this case is composed of two 2 x 4's nailed together. For this reason, only the 4″ masonry section requires a lintel. This type of lintel serves equally well for stone or any other type of masonry veneer.

Steel Channels. Where openings occur in walls having thicknesses of 8″ or more and where the openings are very wide, channels can be used to advantage to support large volumes of masonry and joist loads. In Fig. 17 the channel is shown standing vertically. In such cases a plate (as indicated) is necessary to support the brickwork between the top of the channel and the plate. Above the channel the brickwork is bonded so that its weight is supported by the channel.

Steel I Beams. For wall of 8″ or more in thickness and where the openings are wide or where large amounts of masonry or heavy joist loads must be supported, an **I** beam can be used as a lintel in much the same manner as was explained for the channel in Fig. 17. Or, as shown in Fig. 18, an **I** beam can be used to help support a stone lintel which is

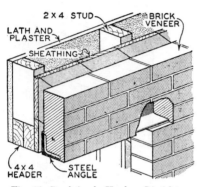

Fig. 16. Steel Angle Used as Lintel in
Brick Veneer Wall Eight Inches
in Thickness

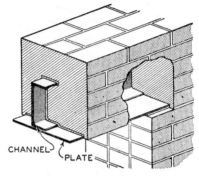

Fig. 17. Channel Used as Lintel in
Walls Eight Inches or More in
Thickness

used for ornamentation. In like manner, a channel could be used in place of an **I** beam in Fig. 18. The shape of the steel selected for cases such as shown in Figs. 17 and 18 depends upon the shapes of the steel available and the amount of room in the wall. Sometimes a channel would fit into spaces such as in Fig. 18 better than an **I** beam. However, either makes a satisfactory lintel.

Steel Angles and Stone. For many buildings where considerable stonework is used for ornamentation on front elevations, stone blocks are required over the heads of window and door openings. In such cases, steel angles or channels in a horizontal position must carry the bulk of the load. Fig. 19 shows a 12″ brick wall where two angles are used in back of the stone. A channel, as shown by dash lines, could be used equally well or a **T** beam in an inverted position would serve the purpose. For very heavy loads, the channel or **T** beam would probably be used because of its stiffness and strength.

Fig. 20 illustrates the use of a reinforced concrete lintel in a concrete block wall faced with a brick veneer. It should be noted that the concrete lintel supports the concrete block portion of the wall while a steel angle supports the brick facing.

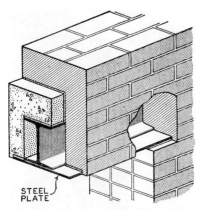

Fig. 18. An **I** Beam Used as Lintel in Walls Eight Inches or More in Thickness

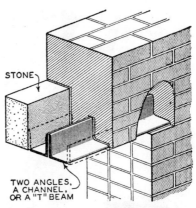

Fig. 19. Illustrating Use of Stone Lintel Backed Up by Two Angles, Channel, or **T** Beam

There are many kinds of lintels and just as many combinations of steel and concrete used in making them. However, the foregoing descriptions and explanations should be sufficient to give the reader a fairly comprehensive knowledge of the most common types in use.

SELECTION OF LINTELS

Selection of Steel-Angle Lintels. In the construction of residences, apartment buildings, and medium-sized stores or industrial buildings, brick walls of from 8″ to 12″ are generally specified. In the case of a brick or stone veneer wall, there will usually be

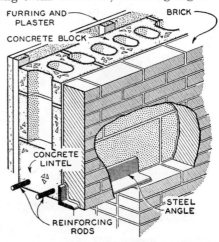

Fig. 20. Reinforced Concrete Lintel and Steel Angle in a Concrete Block Wall with Brick Veneer

just one steel angle or other steel shape in each lintel. Where a wall is of solid masonry, there will be two and sometimes three steel shapes incorporated in each lintel.

In order to understand the selection of lintels, suppose the window in Fig. 9 is in a brick veneer wall, that there are no joists above it, and

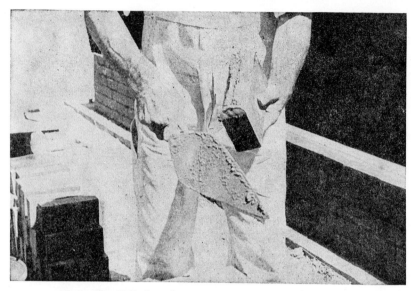

Mortar Should Be Spread over Entire Side of Header Brick before
It Is Placed on Wall To Insure a Complete Bond
Louisville Cement Company, Louisville, Kentucky

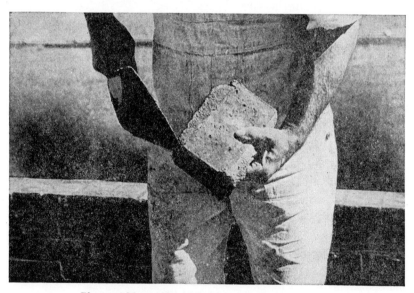

Plenty of Mortar Should Be Placed on Both Sides of the
Closure Brick To Be Placed in a Header Course
Louisville Cement Company, Louisville, Kentucky

that the required lintel has to support only the 4″ brick masonry within the triangle *ABC* above it. The problem is to select a lintel with one steel angle which is strong enough to take care of the job.

The first step in determining what size steel angle to use in the lintel is to find the area of triangle *ABC*. Since the sides and two bottom angles are equal, it is an isosceles triangle. The area of a triangle is equal to one-half of the base multiplied by the altitude or the base multiplied by the altitude and divided by two. In a 45° isosceles triangle, the altitude is equal to one-half of the base. Following these rules, the area of triangle *ABC* is four square feet.

The next step is to find the volume of brickwork in triangle *ABC*. The bricks are 4″ or ⅓′ thick. Therefore, multiplying the area (4 square feet) by ⅓ gives 1⅓ cubic feet. If the weight of brickwork is assumed to be 120 pounds per cubic foot, the weight of the brickwork in triangle *ABC* will be 120 × 1⅓, or 160 pounds.

The final step is the selection of a steel angle which will safely carry the total load of 160 pounds over the 4′0″ of the opening. If Tables I and II are examined, it will be seen that any number of angles of different sizes will be ample. Note the 3″ x 2″ x ¼″ angle in Table II. This angle can safely carry 4,270 pounds over a span of one foot. Over a 4′0″ span it could carry 4,270 ÷ 4, or 1,067.5 pounds. This angle is much stronger than is actually necessary but is selected because with the 3″ leg in a horizontal position, there is good footing for the brickwork. A much smaller angle such as a 2½″ x 2″ x ⅛″ could be used otherwise.

A slightly different problem is found in making the steel angle selection for the lintel of the door in Fig. 10. It can be assumed that the wall is one of brick and is 8″ in thickness, that there are no joist loads, and that the lintel required has only the spandrel section *CDAB* to support.

The first step is to find the area of the spandrel section *CDAB*. For the purpose of this problem it can be assumed that the distance from line *CD* to line *AB* is an even six feet. The area therefore is 4′0″ x 6′0″, or 24 square feet. The volume of this area is ⅔′ (8″ = ⅔′) × 24 or 16 cubic feet. This number multiplied by the weight of brickwork per cubic foot gives an answer of 1,920 pounds as the weight of area *CDAB*. Again, because of so little weight to be supported, any one of many angles can be selected. Since two angles will be needed because of the 8″ thickness of the wall, it is permissible to assume that half of the load or approximately 1,000 pounds will be carried by each of the two angles. Therefore, the 3″ x 2″ x ¼″ angle selected for the lintel of the window in Fig. 9 will be of sufficient size. The use of two angles, as shown in Fig. 15, gives adequate support and provides a 6″ surface for the brickwork.

The calculations involved in selecting a steel angle for a lintel are further complicated when joists have their bearing in that section of

TABLE I.   ALLOWABLE UNIFORM LOAD FOR
ANGLES IN THOUSANDS OF POUNDS

Shorter Leg Horizontal

Maximum Bending Stress, 16,000 Pounds per Square Inch

SIZE, INCHES	THICK-NESS, INCHES	SAFE LOAD FOR 1-FOOT SPAN	SIZE, INCHES	THICK-NESS, INCHES	SAFE LOAD FOR 1-FOOT SPAN
8 x 8	1⅛	186.99	5 x 4	⅞	53.23
	½	89.28		⅜	24.96
6 x 6	1	91.41	5 x 3½	⅞	52.05
	⅜	37.65		⁵⁄₁₆	20.69
5 x 5	1	61.87	5 x 3	¹³⁄₁₆	47.47
	⅜	25.81		⁵⁄₁₆	20.16
4 x 4	¹³⁄₁₆	32.11	4½ x 3	¹³⁄₁₆	38.61
	¼	11.20		⁵⁄₁₆	16.43
3½ x 3½	¹³⁄₁₆	24.00	4 x 3½	¹³⁄₁₆	31.15
	¼	8.43		⁵⁄₁₆	13.44
3 x 3	⅝	13.87	4 x 3	¹³⁄₁₆	30.61
	¼	6.19		¼	10.67
2½ x 2½	½	7.79	3½ x 3	¹³⁄₁₆	23.47
	⅛	2.13		¼	8.32
2 x 2	⁷⁄₁₆	4.27	3½ x 2½	¹¹⁄₁₆	19.73
	⅛	1.39		¼	8.00
1¾ x 1¾	⁷⁄₁₆	3.20	3 x 2½	⁹⁄₁₆	12.27
	⅛	1.07		¼	5.97
1½ x 1½	⅜	2.03	3 x 2	½	10.67
	⅛	0.77		¼	5.76
1¼ x 1¼	⁵⁄₁₆	1.17	2½ x 2	½	7.47
	⅛	0.52		⅛	2.13
1 x 1	¼	0.60	2½ x 1½	⁵⁄₁₆	4.69
	⅛	0.33		³⁄₁₆	2.99
8 x 6	1	161.17	2¼ x 1½	½	5.76
	⁷⁄₁₆	75.41		³⁄₁₆	2.45
8 x 3½	1	146.03	2 x 1½	⅜	3.63
	⁷⁄₁₆	68.80		⅛	1.39
7 x 3½	1	112.85	2 x 1¼	¼	2.45
	⅜	46.19		³⁄₁₆	1.92
6 x 4	1	85.55	1¾ x 1¼	¼	1.92
	⅜	35.41		⅛	1.00
6 x 3½	1	83.52	1½ x 1¼	⁵⁄₁₆	1.71
	⁵⁄₁₆	29.23		³⁄₁₆	1.07

wall supported by the lintel. The lintel then carries the weight of the brickwork as well as the load from the joists.

As an example, assume that in addition to the weight of the masonry work as illustrated in the last problem (Fig. 10), the lintel must support joist loads from the second floor. This situation is illustrated in Figs. 11 and 21. Four joists spaced on 16″ centers have their bearing in the wall directly over the door. Since these joists are 14′0″ in length, the floor area involved is 56 square feet. If the total live and dead floor load is assumed to be 60 pounds per square foot, the total floor load supported by the four joists is 56 × 60, or 3,360 pounds. Half of this load will be supported by interior bearing partitions and the balance by the lintel over the door. The total load which the lintel must support is one-half of 3,360, or 1,680 pounds + 1,920 pounds (the weight of the brickwork, same as for the last problem), or 3,600 pounds. By referring to Table I, it can be seen that a 3½″ x 3½″ x ¼″ angle will safely carry approximately 2,100 pounds across a 4′0″ span. Two such angles should be adequate to carry the load.

TABLE II. ALLOWABLE UNIFORM LOAD FOR ANGLES WITH LEGS
OF UNEQUAL LENGTH IN THOUSANDS OF POUNDS
Longer Leg Horizontal
Maximum Bending stress, 16,000 Pounds per Square Inch

Size, Inches	Thickness, Inches	Safe Load for 1-Foot Span	Size, Inches	Thickness, Inches	Safe Load for 1-Foot Span
8 x 6	1	95.15	3½ x 3	13/16	17.60
	7/16	45.12		¼	6.19
8 x 3½	1	32.21	3½ x 2½	11/16	10.56
	7/16	15.57		¼	4.37
7 x 3½	1	31.57	3 x 2	9/16	8.75
	3/8	13.44		¼	4.27
6 x 4	1	40.43		½	5.01
	3/8	17.07		¼	2.77
6 x 3½	1	30.93	2½ x 2	½	4.91
	5/16	11.09		1/8	1.49
5 x 4	7/8	35.31	2½ x 1½	5/16	1.81
	3/8	16.75		3/16	1.17
5 x 3½	7/8	26.88	2¼ x 1½	½	2.77
	5/16	10.88		3/16	1.17
5 x 3	13/16	18.56	2 x 1½	3/8	2.13
	5/16	8.00		1/8	0.80
4½ x 3	13/16	18.24	2 x 1¼	¼	1.04
	5/16	8.00		3/16	0.80
4 x 3½	13/16	24.53	1¾ x 1¼	¼	1.01
	5/16	10.67		1/8	0.56
4 x 3	13/16	17.92	1½ x 1¼	5/16	1.17
	¼	6.40		3/16	0.78

Two or more windows over a window or door opening in a wall also increase the complexities involved in selecting the proper steel angle or angles to be used in the lintel. In order to illustrate the methods used, it must be assumed that windows *3*, *4*, and *5* are in a 12″ brick wall, the second floor joists spaced on 12″ centers, and that the total floor load is 150 pounds per square foot.

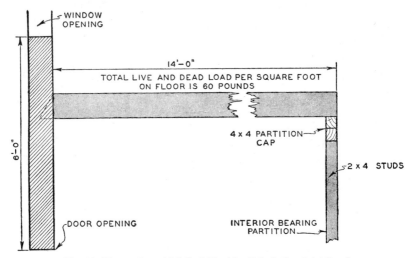

Fig. 21. Illustration of Method Used in Calculating Joist Loads

The first step in the solution is to find the total weight of the brickwork. Column *GHEF* is 3′0″ wide and 11′0″ high and has an area of 33 square feet. The two small columns, *LMJE* and *OPFK*, are each 1′0″ wide and 6′0″ long, making an area of 12 square feet. The total area of the brickwork is 45 square feet. Since the wall is 12″ thick, the volume of the wall will be 45 cubic feet. The total weight of the brickwork is 120 × 45, or 5,400 pounds. The floor supported by the joists over window *5* is 5′0″ wide and 12′0″ long. Its area, therefore, will be 60 square feet. The total floor load will be 150 × 60, or 9,000 pounds. Since only half of this load will be carried by the lintel, the total weight on the lintel will be 4,500 + 5,400, or 9,900 pounds.

Since the wall is 12″ thick, three angles will be required as shown in Fig. 13. Each angle will be required to support one-third of the total load, or 3,300 pounds. Table I shows that a 5″ x 3″ x $\frac{5}{16}$″ angle will support 20,160 pounds over a 1'0" span and 4,032 pounds over a 5'0" span. Three of these angles will be satisfactory for use.

A load of the size just calculated in the above example could be carried economically by a steel I beam. Computation shows that a 5" I beam weighing 10 pounds per foot would carry the 9,900-pound load safely over the 5'0" span. If the I beam were used, a 12" × ½" steel plate would be necessary to support the brickwork below the top of the beam. This is illustrated in Figs. 17 and 18.

When a lintel similar to the one shown in Fig. 14 is used, the selection procedure is the same as was described for steel angles except that the total weights and loads are divided between the wood beam and the steel angle. If the 4 x 6 wood beam is expected to handle half the load, then it and the steel angle must be selected on that basis.

When extremely heavy loads occur over wide openings and where heavy floor loads are expected, the use of I beams, channels, and combinations of them are sometimes necessary. Large lintels such as these are selected as was described for the procedures involved in selecting beams. If complicated loadings are encountered, it is recommended that a structural engineer be consulted.

The deflection of steel lintels should be carefully considered when making selections for specific job purposes, just as it was an important factor in selecting steel beams. The tendency for steel angles and beams to bend under stress can be offset by using an angle or beam which is slightly heavier than is absolutely necessary. Their stiffness will generally be sufficient to prevent any appreciable deflection.

HOW TO SET LINTELS

Steel Lintels. When the brickwork has been laid up to the window height, care should be taken to smooth the joints so that no mortar extends up beyond the horizontal surface of the bricks where the lintel will be set. This will avoid the presence of uneven spots in the bearing area at a later time when the lintels are lifted into place.

In most cases, the steel angles selected for a lintel such as shown in Fig. 12 have horizontal legs of such a length that they do not quite reach the edge of the brick wall. This is illustrated more clearly in Fig. 22. Since the outside face of a brick wall would not look well if the edge of the angle extended to the edge of the bricks, the length of the legs is an important factor in selection.

The length of the angles should be sufficient to allow at least 4″ of bearing on both sides of the opening as shown in Fig. 22. For openings larger than 3′0″, and where loads are heavy, the bearing surface should be increased up to 12 inches. Bearing surfaces are important for two reasons. Ample bearing surface prevents any tendency for the ends

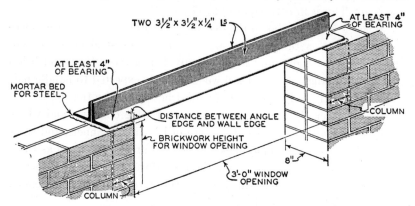

TWO 3½″ x 3½″ x ¼″ Ls

AT LEAST 4″ OF BEARING

AT LEAST 4″ OF BEARING

MORTAR BED FOR STEEL

DISTANCE BETWEEN ANGLE EDGE AND WALL EDGE

BRICKWORK HEIGHT FOR WINDOW OPENING

COLUMN

8″

3′-0″ WINDOW OPENING

COLUMN

Fig. 22. Method of Placing Steel Angle Lintels

of the angles to rise upward and crack the brickwork over them. In addition, ample bearing surface provides large columns of brickwork (see Fig. 22) which support the angles and the loads on them.

Angles should be placed back to back as indicated in Figs. 12 and 22, and centered carefully over the walls. Before finally setting the angles, a mortar bed should be spread over the bearing areas. This provides a cushion for the angles and makes it possible to set them in the correct position horizontally and vertically. The angles should be pressed down until the mortar bed is the same thickness approximately as the brick joints.

When setting lintels such as shown in Fig. 14, the same procedure as just explained is followed. The wood beam is set on a mortar bed along with the angle. Where two angles are used as illustrated in Fig. 15 the first or lower angle is set and the brickwork laid up to the point where the second angle is set.

For a part stone lintel such as shown in Fig. 19, the stone is placed first on a bed of mortar the same thickness as for the brick joints. The angles, **T** beam, or channel, is then placed as explained for any of the other typical examples.

Where an **I** beam or channel is used as a lintel, as in Fig. 17, the plate is set first following the procedures already described, making certain it is level at both bearing points. The channel or **I** beam is then placed on the plate and the brickwork laid on and around both members. When the channels or **I** beams for this kind of lintel are longer than the plate and extend over the brickwork at either end, the ends of the member are set in mortar beds in the usual manner.

CHAPTER IV

How To Lay Bricks

PROPER JOINTS IN BRICKWORK

As bricklayers are laying up walls, for example, they should keep in mind that unless the mortar joints are made *properly*, the mortar will fail to some extent, in one or all of its required functions. Mortar joints must be made *carefully* and properly. The importance of this cannot be overemphasized. Excellent bricks and excellent mortar cannot produce good walls or any other structural items unless the mortar is properly applied so that each succeeding course has the proper bond.

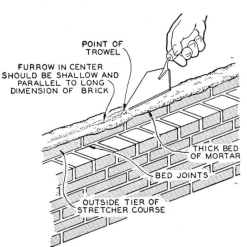

Fig. 1. Proper Bed Joints in Walls

Bed Joints in Stretcher Courses. A bed joint, as illustrated in Fig. 1, is a horizontal joint upon which bricks rest. Bed joints are important from the standpoints of bonding bricks together, creating equal pressure throughout a wall, and making the wall moistureproof and airproof.

Mortar for bed joints should be spread thick as indicated by the thick bed of mortar under the trowel in Fig. 1. The mortar can be one inch or more in thickness. It is customary to run the point of the trowel along the mortar, as shown in the illustration, to make a furrow. This furrow should be along the middle of the mortar bed and should be shallow, not deep. It is not advisable to spread bed mortar more than a distance of four or five brick lengths in advance

The labels within Fig. 1 read:
POINT OF TROWEL
FURROW IN CENTER SHOULD BE SHALLOW AND PARALLEL TO LONG DIMENSION OF BRICK
THICK BED OF MORTAR
BED JOINTS
OUTSIDE TIER OF STRETCHER COURSE

of laying. This is especially important during hot and dry weather. By spreading the bed not more than a few brick lengths in advance of laying, the mortar remains soft and plastic and allows bricks to be laid (bedded) easily and properly.

Head Joints in Stretcher Courses. A head joint, as illustrated in Fig. 3, is a vertical joint which joins bricks together at their ends. Head joints are also important, especially from the standpoint of preventing cracks in the wall and making the wall moistureproof and airproof.

Head joints, like bed joints, must be *completely filled with mortar.* There are different ways in which this can be accomplished. Plenty

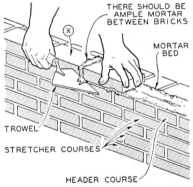

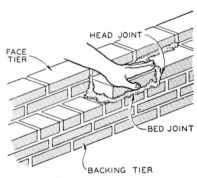

Fig. 2. Proper Head Joints in Walls   Fig. 3. Proper Bed and Head Joints for Backing

of mortar, as thick as will stick, should be thrown on the end of each brick to be placed. This should be done in such a way that the mortar will be scraped off the trowel by the bottom edge of the end of each brick. The bricks can then be placed on the mortar bed and pushed into place, as shown in Fig. 2, so that the excess mortar squeezes out at the head joint and at the side of the wall. Or, a dab of mortar may first be spotted on the corner of the brick, such as brick X in Fig. 2, already in place. This is followed by placing additional mortar on the end of the brick to be laid. The brick to be laid is then pushed into position.

Both of the methods described in the previous paragraph succeed in making a full head joint. These methods are the *only* methods a good bricklayer should use.

Bed and Head Joints for Backing in Stretcher Courses. Fig. 3 shows part of a wall in which the face tier has been laid up ahead of the backing tier. The bed and head joints here are also important.

The best method for making good bed and head joints as backing is laid is as follows: A large trowelful of mortar should be thrown at the place where backing bricks are to be laid. Plenty of mortar should be used—all that can be carried by the large-sized trowel. Then the bricks should be shoved into this deep mortar so that it oozes out from the bed and head joints as shown in Fig. 3. This method makes absolutely certain that joints are full of mortar at every point.

Cross Joints in Header Courses. Cross joints also should be carefully made to assure their being *absolutely filled with mortar.*

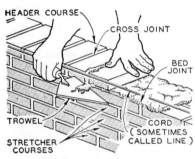

Fig. 4. Proper Cross Joints in Walls

First, plenty of mortar should be spread, several brick widths in advance, to form the bed joint. This mortar should be up to an inch thick and evenly spread. Before each header brick is laid, the edge shown in Fig. 4, the header should be entirely covered with all the mortar that will stick to it. Then, as shown in Fig. 4, the header should be shoved into place so that mortar oozes out above the cross joint as well as at the bed joint. The excess mortar is scraped off with the trowel.

Closure Joints in Stretcher Courses. The last brick to be placed in a stretcher course must be laid so that both head joints are completely filled with mortar.

With the bed joint mortar already in place, the first step in laying a closure is to apply plenty of mortar to the ends of bricks X and Y in Fig. 5, which are already in place. Also, ample mortar should be thrown on the two ends of the brick to be placed. The mortar should entirely cover the two ends. Finally, the closure should be laid as indicated without disturbing the brick already in place.

Closure Joints in Header Courses. The laying of a closure brick in a header course is illustrated in Fig. 6. Before laying the closure brick, plenty of mortar should be placed on the sides of both bricks

Joints in Header Courses Should Be Completely Filled with Mortar So It
Oozes Out at the Top of the Joint When Brick Are Placed
Louisville Cement Company, Louisville, Kentucky

Dabs of Mortar Spotted on Corners of Brick Cannot Fill the Cross Joints,
and Slushing Joints After Brick Are Placed Will Not Fill Voids
Louisville Cement Company, Louisville, Kentucky

Plenty of Mortar Should Be Placed on the End of the Brick in Place,
To Fill Joint Completely When the Next Brick Is Laid
Louisville Cement Company, Louisville, Kentucky

Bricks Must Be Laid True to the Line When Originally Placed, for Shifting
Brick Breaks Bond and Causes Cracks between the Brick and Mortar
Louisville Cement Company, Louisville, Kentucky

already in place. Also, mortar should be carefully and amply spread on both edges of the closure brick so that the edges are completely covered to a thickness up to an inch. Then the closure should be laid without disturbing the bricks already in place.

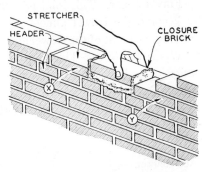

No matter what kind of brickwork is being laid—thick joints or thin—the joints should be completely filled. Any deviation from this rule is poor bricklaying.

Finishes of Joints. • The finishes of joints at the surface of the

Fig. 5. Proper Closure Joints in Walls

brickwork is for the purpose of making the brickwork more waterproof and pleasing to the eye. Several types of joint finishes are employed. A few typical joint finishes are shown in Fig. 7. There are other types, but none are in common enough use to include here.

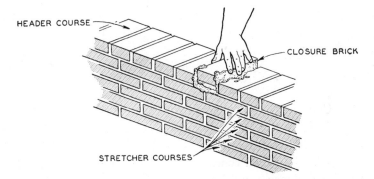

Fig. 6. Proper Closure Joints in Walls

The practice of finishing a joint simply by drawing one edge of the trowel along it and scraping the excess mortar off is not recommended. For example, suppose a bricklayer finished the joint, in (A) of Fig. 7, by such a process. If he drew the trowel upward there probably would be a crack between the mortar and the brick at Y. If he pushed the trowel downward, the crack might occur at X. Whichever way the edge of a trowel is drawn across a joint, the joint is left in an improper condition. The remedy is to use the trowel or a pointing tool as explained in the following descriptions.

FLUSH JOINT. This joint is shown in (A) of Fig. 7. It can be made by keeping the trowel almost parallel to the face of the wall while drawing the point of the trowel along the joint.

WEATHER JOINT. This joint is shown in (B) of Fig. 7. It is a joint designed to shed water more easily from the surface of the wall. This joint is made by striking it downward with the top edge of the trowel. In other words, the top of the mortar joint is mashed in with the top edge of the trowel.

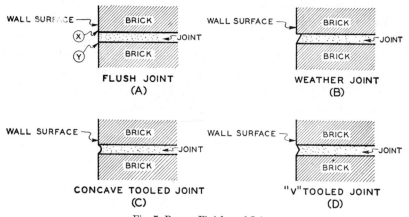

Fig. 7. Proper Finishes of Joints

V AND CONCAVE TOOLED JOINTS. These joints are shown in (C) and (D) of Fig. 7. Special pointing tools are required to make them. Excess mortar is removed with the trowel after which the joint tools are employed. The V and concave tooled joints are perhaps the best joints under ordinary conditions. The finishing of joints should be done before the mortar hardens to any appreciable extent.

Parging. Parging, or the plastering of brick tiers, is a good means of making walls more moistureproof and airproof. Fig. 8 shows a wall being back-plastered. The plaster is applied to the back of the facing tier. This is done between header courses and should be about ⅜″ thick. Regular mortar can be used for the purpose. This back-plastering can be omitted if desired and the backing tier laid as indicated in Fig. 3.

Back-up Units Should Be Backplastered (Parged) with Mortar before the Face Brick Are Laid

Louisville Cement Company, Louisville, Kentucky

Thicknesses of Mortar Joints. The matter of joint thicknesses cannot be stated very well as a hard and fast rule because of the many possible variables which are encountered.

Bricks made by either the stiff- or soft-mud process are likely to be somewhat irregular in shape and thus must be laid up using mortar joints approximately ½″ thick. This varies according to the condition of the brick. The thinner mortar joints, such as ¼″, are the strongest and should be used whenever possible. Bricks manufactured by the pressed process are likely to be regular enough in shape to allow the use of ¼″ mortar joints.

Fig. 8. Parging

When walls have face tiers made of common or rough-textured bricks, the mortar joints in these face tiers are sometimes made up to ¾″ in thickness. In such cases, the joints in the backing tiers are adjusted either by additional courses or thicker mortar joints than usual so as to bring the two tiers at the same level at the header courses.

When colored mortar is used in face tier joints, the thickness of the joints is frequently decided by the effect of the color in the wall surface. When light-colored bricks are used as facing, thin, colored mortar joints give the principal effect. Usually, however, the wider the colored mortar joint, the more colorful the wall will be.

For ordinary brick masonry, the mortar joints should be made as near to ¼″ as possible.

Joints for Firebrick. Special fire clay mortar is required for firebrick. Such mortar can be purchased ready to mix for use. Very little mortar should be used in firebrick joints. If such bricks do not fit snugly together, one or more of them should be cut until they do fit.

Twelve-Inch Wall with Face Tier Laid Ahead of Backing Tier
Detroit Building Trades School, Detroit, Michigan

HOW TO ERECT BRICK WALLS

When the commonly used kinds of brick are known, when the specific uses of such brick are known, and when the typical brick masonry details are understood and can be visualized, the next logical step is to learn how this kind of masonry is actually laid. The processes or techniques involved, while not extremely difficult, do require careful study and then a great deal of actual practice. The aim of the following illustrations and explanations is to prepare the reader for the actual practice phase of his training. The following examples represent the kind of bricklaying most commonly encountered by inexperienced bricklayers.

Laying an 8″ Common Bond Brick Wall. This wall of common brick has ½″ joints between the units. The bricks are laid in common bond illustrated in (A) and (B) of Fig. 4, Chapter III. Note in (B) that there are six courses of stretchers, then one course of headers. In other words, there is a header course every seventh course. The positions of the bricks in a common bond wall are indicated in both (A) and (B).

Fig. 9 shows more details of an 8″ brick wall laid in common bond. The sketch at (C) illustrates a corner and shows three courses of the two tiers required. It can be seen that the first course is a header course, as is generally required. The sketch at (B) shows the details of this course. Along the lengths of walls, headers are easy to place, but at the corners, closures must be used in order to fill up the space. The use of three-quarter and quarter closures permits the filling of the corners as shown in the sketch. The second course consists of stretchers which can be laid without the use of fractional closures. This can be seen in sketch (A). The third, fourth, fifth, and sixth courses, although not shown in Fig. 9, also consist of stretchers laid so as to break joints. For example, note in sketch (C) how the corner bricks for courses two and three are alternated. This alternating of stretchers, or breaking of joints, can be seen to good advantage at (B) in Fig. 4, Chapter III.

In many buildings, 12″ brick walls laid in common bond are required. Fig. 10 illustrates the positions of the bricks and fractional closures in such a wall.

When masons erect brick walls, corners are laid up in advance of the wall lengths between the corners. This practice affords them the opportunity of using the corners as a guide in laying the balance of the walls. In Fig. 11, assume that the foundation shown in (A) has been poured, that it has been designed so as to fit an even number of bricks (as explained previously in Fig. 4, Chapter III), and that it is perfectly level and ready for an 8″ common brick wall to be laid on it. The bricks at either end illustrate the corners which bricklayers always lay up before laying bricks the full length of the wall. The sketch at (B) shows one of the corners laid up and racked so that other bricks can be bonded into them when the balance of the wall is laid. Note that only the face tier is laid in these corners. It should also be noted that the corners are laid up to a height of the second header course or a distance of seven courses.

In (A) of Fig. 12 is shown a plan view of the same foundation illustrated in Fig. 11. Before the corners are started, bricklayers lay dry bricks (without mortar) along the wall to test its length in terms of bond. As shown in (A), the wall length is just right in terms of whole bricks. A stretcher course is used for such a test.

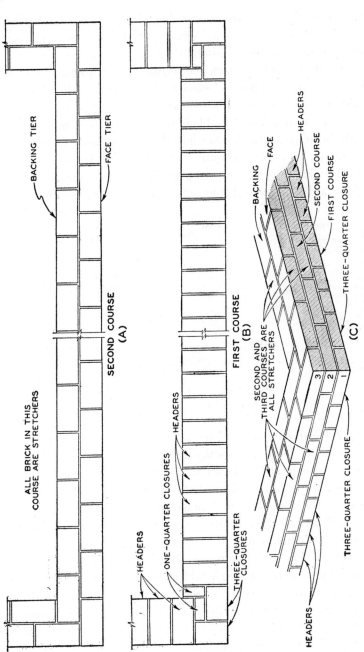

Fig. 9. Common Bond in Eight-Inch Wall

In (B) of Fig. 12 is shown the first step in laying up a corner. Mortar should be spread evenly, directly on the concrete of the foundation top and should be at least ¾″ deep.

In (C) of Fig. 12 is shown the second step. The mason cuts two bricks to make three-quarter closures as shown in (B) of Fig. 9. Closure *1* is laid on the mortar and pressed down with the hand until the joint becomes ½″ as required. The blade of the trowel is sometimes used to gently hammer the brick down into the mortar. Next, mortar should be thrown on the end of closure *2* as previously explained for head joints. This closure is then shoved gently into place up against closure *1* to form a ½″ horizontal joint with the foundation and also a ½″

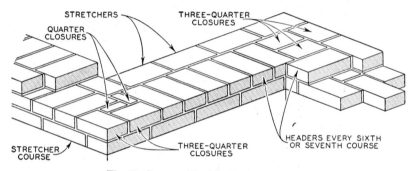

Fig. 10. Common Bond in Twelve-Inch Wall

vertical or head joint with closure *1*. This should be done as explained for Fig. 2. Clean off the excess mortar which oozed out from the horizontal and head joints by holding the trowel as shown in Fig. 2. The level of closures *1* and *2* should be checked, using a plumb rule laid in the position of the dash lines shown in (C) of Fig. 12. If the bricks are not exactly level, they are hammered gently with the trowel until they are. The edges of both bricks also must be flush with the outside surfaces of the foundation.

In (D) of Fig. 12 is shown the third step. Brick *3* should have mortar thrown on its edge and laid as shown. Check its level using the plumb rule in the position of the dash line and make sure its end is flush with the foundation. Brick *4* is laid in the same manner and its level, etc., checked. The quarter-closures should next be cut and mortar applied to them as explained for closures relative to Figs. 5

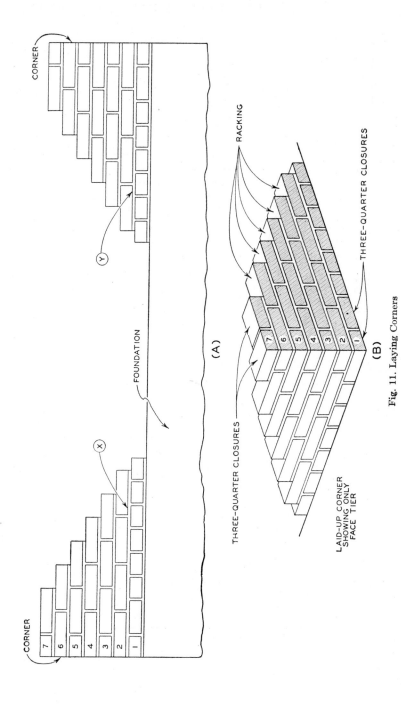

Fig. 11. Laying Corners

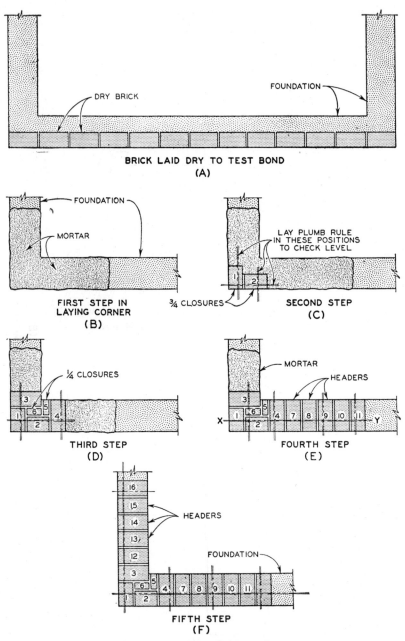

BRICK LAID DRY TO TEST BOND
(A)

FIRST STEP IN
LAYING CORNER
(B)

SECOND STEP
(C)

THIRD STEP
(D)

FOURTH STEP
(E)

FIFTH STEP
(F)

Fig. 12. Laying First Course at Corners

and 6. Remove all excess mortar and be sure that the quarter-closures do not extend above the top levels of the surrounding bricks.

In (E) of Fig. 12 is shown the fourth step. The edge of brick *7* has mortar thrown on it and is then shoved into position as shown in Fig. 4. All excess mortar is removed with the trowel. Bricks *8, 9, 10,* and *11* are laid in like manner. The level should be checked by placing the plumb rule in the position of the dash line *XY* and in the opposite direction, indicated by the second set of dash lines. The matter of flushness with the foundation also should be checked.

In (F) of Fig. 12 is shown the fifth step. Bricks *12, 13, 14, 15,* and *16* are placed in the same manner as bricks *7* through *11*.

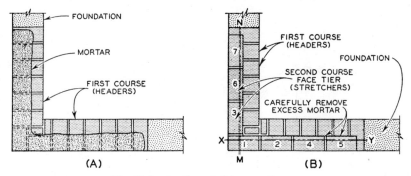

Fig. 13. Laying Second Course at Corners

The number of bricks to lay in the first course for the corners can be determined from a sketch such as shown in (B) of Fig. 11.

The second course for the corner, as shown in (B) and (A) of Figs. 11 and 9 respectively, should be composed of stretchers. But only the facing tier should be laid at this stage of the wall construction.

In (A) of Fig. 13 is shown the first step in laying the second course of stretchers. Mortar should be spread over the first course to a depth of at least ¾ inch. The furrow in the mortar, as explained for bed joints and as illustrated in Fig. 1, should be shallow. Brick *1* should be laid on the mortar and gently shoved or hammered down until the mortar joint is ½ inch. Mortar should be thrown on the end of brick *2* and the brick shoved into position. Remove excess mortar as shown in Fig. 2. The joint should be checked for thickness. Bricks *3, 4, 5, 6,* and *7* should be laid in the same manner. Next, the level and plumbness should be checked. The check for level is made by placing the plumb rule in the positions of dash lines *XY* and *MN*. The plumb check is made by placing the plumb rule in a vertical position against the foundation and bricks at several points.

Note: The number of bricks necessary in the second course for the corners can be determined from the sketch shown in (B) of Fig. 11.

The balance of the courses (see [B] of Fig. 11) are laid in the same manner. Care must be exercised in constantly checking the level, and after the first few courses, the plumbness of the rising corner. This is especially important because the wall between corners is laid using the corners as a guide. If the courses are not plumb, the bricks must be moved in or out until the plumb check is perfect. It is not

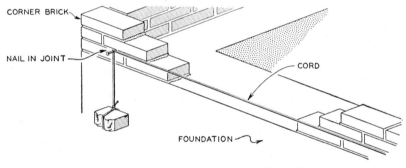

CORNER BRICK

NAIL IN JOINT

CORD

FOUNDATION

Fig. 14. Cord Used as Guide in Laying Every Course

good practice to move bricks once they have been laid, so special care should be taken to lay the corner plumb as it progresses.

The joints should be well pointed before the mortar has set. The outside joints are finished using a pointing tool. The inside joints can be finished flush with the trowel.

The foregoing procedure should be followed in laying up all corners.

In order to lay the face tier bricks along the wall between the corners, a cord should be stretched to serve as a guide for each course. Note Fig. 14. To place the cord in proper position for laying the first course between corners, drive nails into mortar joints as shown by *X* and *Y* in (A) of Fig. 11. The cord is wound around these nails, as shown in Fig. 14, with a weight to hold the cord at each nail. As shown in this illustration, the cord should not quite touch the outer corner of the corner brick.

With the cord in place between nails X and Y in (A) of Fig. 11, the first, or header, course can be laid between the two corners. The joints are all cross joints and the mortar should be applied and the bricks laid as previously explained for such joints and as illustrated in Fig. 4. As each brick is laid, its outer and upper corner should not quite touch the cord. The cord thus serves as a guide in keeping all bricks level and the wall plumb. For the second course between corners, the cord should be moved up one course. This course consists of stretchers which should have mortar applied to them as previously explained relative to bed and head joints and be laid as explained for Fig. 5.

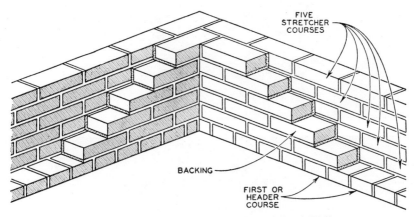

Fig. 15. Backing for Corner of Eight-Inch Brick Wall

The face joints should be tool pointed and the inner joints troweled smooth prior to the time the mortar sets.

When the face tier for two corners and the intervening wall have been laid up to the height of the second header course (six courses as shown in (A) of Fig. 11), the backing tier is laid. It is best to lay the backing bricks first for the two corners, as shown in Fig. 15, and to lay the balance of the backing after that. It is not necessary to use a cord for the backing except for 12″ walls.

Apply mortar to backing bricks and lay them as explained for Fig. 3. Closures for backing tier courses should be laid as previously explained.

When the backing for the first wall is complete up to header height,

Cross and Bed Joints Must Be Kept Uniform and Bonded
Tightly at Corners, as in Wall Above
Laid in Flemish Spiral Bond
Detroit Building Trades School, Detroit, Michigan

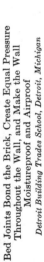

Bed Joints Bond the Brick, Create Equal Pressure
Throughout the Wall, and Make the Wall
Moistureproof and Airproof
Detroit Building Trades School, Detroit, Michigan

another corner, adjacent to one of the corners already completed, can be laid up and the same procedure followed.

When all walls have been completed to the second header height, corners are again laid up to the third header height and the same process repeated. This general procedure is followed until the proper total height of the wall has been reached. Provisions for window and door openings are discussed in advanced examples.

Laying an 8″ Common Bond Wall with Common and Face Brick. This type of wall is laid following exactly the same procedure just explained for a common bond wall in common brick, except for the following differences:

First, the face tier is laid using face bricks.

Second, the headers are all laid using face brick.

Third, the backing stretcher courses are laid using common brick.

Fourth, face brick generally require much more careful joint pointing.

Fifth, there may be some backing tier joint variation if the face brick tier must be laid using very thin joints. In such cases, bricklayers sometimes use one less course of bricks in the backing tier with much thicker joints. The main object is to make both tiers even at every header course. The joint thickness required can be determined by trial.

Laying Window Openings in 8″ Common Bond Brick Walls. If one or more windows are required in a brick wall, the bricklayer must plan for them in advance in order that one course of bricks will be at exactly the right height above the foundation for the window sills. Note window in wall shown in (A) of Fig. 4, Chapter III. Not counting the rowlock headers, there were just 12 courses up to the bottom level of the sill. By measuring the vertical distances that window sills must be above foundations, bricklayers can determine how many courses that distance is equal to. This can be done by measuring such a distance on a wall already laid and then counting the courses. Architects generally consider brick courses when they determine window location dimensions, but it is wise for bricklayers to check for their own convenience.

When a brick wall has been laid up to sill height, the rowlock sill, shown in (A) of Fig. 4, Chapter III, is laid. The rowlock course should be sharply pitched and should take up verticle space equivalent to two courses. When laying the rowlock course, ample mortar should be used under and between bricks. The surface joints must be very carefully tooled to make them waterproof.

After the rowlock sill has set, the window frame is placed on the sill and temporarily supported by wood braces. The bricklayer's next concern is to lay up the surrounding wall so that a course of brick near the top of the frame comes at a level not more than $\frac{1}{4}''$ higher than the frame. To accomplish this, he marks with a pencil the position of the top course on both sides of the frame. Below these marks, he makes other marks indicating where each header course should be. Sometimes mortar joints have to be varied a little in order to bring header courses to the marks on the frame.

Bricks are laid on both sides of the frame using the cord stretched across the frame opening as previously explained. If window locations have been well planned by the architect, the bond in the face tier will not be disturbed. In other cases, bricks of the face tier may have to be cut.

When the wall has been built up to the height of the frame, mortar is applied about $\frac{1}{2}''$ deep to the top of the frame and to the wall on both sides of the frame. Steel lintels are then placed over the window opening and bedded in the mortar. Once the two pieces of the lintel are in place, the wall is continued on above them. The bricks are cut so they will fit around the lintels. (See Fig. 5, Chapter III.)

Laying Door Openings in 8″ Common Bond Brick Walls. Practically the same procedure is followed in laying bricks around door openings as explained for window openings.

Note the wood brick grounds shown in (B) of Fig. 4, Chapter III. These pieces of wood are cut to the size of a half-closure and then laid into the various courses, using mortar the same as for the clay brick. When the wall is complete and has set, the door frame is secured to the wood brick by means of nails or screws.

Laying a 4″ Brick Veneer Wall on a Wood Frame. Brick veneer generally consists of one tier with the bricks laid in stretcher bond.

The laying of brick veneer follows closely the procedure explained for 8″ walls except that no backing or headers are used and metal ties are employed to secure the veneer to the frame wall. Corners should be laid up seven or eight courses high and a cord should be used to guide the laying of intervening courses. The window frames are already in place when the veneer is started so the bricklayer can judge easily where the last course before the rowlock sill must be placed in terms of distance above the foundation.

The soldier course (Fig. 3, Chapter III) is composed of three-quarter closures or, if desirable, the course can be laid using specially made bricks about 5″ or 6″ long. Fig. 16 shows how queen closures are used at the corners to preserve good appearance.

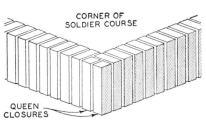

Fig. 16. Corner of Brick Veneer Soldier Course Showing Method of Placing Brick

The soldier course is laid in much the same manner as explained for Fig. 30 in (A), (B), (C), etc. Following this, the courses of stretchers are laid as was explained for (A) and (B) in Fig. 13.

Metal ties must be installed as the corners and intervening wall courses are laid, spaced as previously explained. Care should be taken to nail the ties in such positions that the nails will penetrate the studs and not just the sheathing. This will insure their holding firmly. Laying bricks around and over door and window openings is carried on as described for the 8″ wall. Joints must be carefully tooled so as to add to the good appearance of the wall.

WETTING BRICKS PRIOR TO LAYING

When bricks are laid during warm weather, especially during hot and dry weather, they should be thoroughly wetted but not soaked to the saturation point just prior to the time they are laid. The wetting can be done with a hose or some form of water sprinkler which will just wet the bricks enough so that they look wet all over their surfaces.

There are four reasons for wetting bricks just prior to their laying:

a) The bricks will tend to more evenly spread the mortar under them (this is known as bedding) and thus facilitate a better mortar joint.

b) The bricks will adhere better to the mortar.

c) A dry brick will quickly absorb water from the mortar. This is particularly dangerous when using cement mortar which will not properly dry (set) unless it dries slowly and in a moist condition. The danger is not so pronounced when lime mortar is used as this type of mortar sets by oxidation.

d) Wetting bricks washes the kiln dust from them. A clean brick will produce a better joint or bond with the mortar.

When bricks are laid in cold weather, they should not be wetted.

LAYING BRICKS IN COLD WEATHER

It is best not to lay bricks in cold weather but when it cannot be avoided, the following directions should be followed.

In contrast to the wetting procedures used when laying bricks in hot and dry summer weather, bricks laid during cold weather must be absolutely dry. If possible, they should be warmed before being used. Mortar should be made using hot water and hot sand. Care should be taken not to use hot lime in making mortar because when hot it is not completely slaked and in such condition would cause undesirable results. If salt is added to the mortar water as a means of preventing freezing, it is possible that some efflorescence will occur.

MAINTENANCE OF BRICK WALLS

Repointing Old Brickwork. •Old brick walls which have been exposed to the weather for many years may need repointing as a means of improving their appearance and to make them more watertight and airtight.•This is necessary because the original mortar in the joints weathers away due to the effects of rain, wind, heat, and freezing. Repointing is not difficult.

The first step in repointing is to clean out the old mortar in the joints to a depth of at least ⅛ inch. The old mortar can be loosened with the small end of the hammer, then scraped out with pointing tools made for that purpose. Also, a thin chisel can be used with a hammer to loosen and remove the old mortar to the desired depth. A stiff brush should be used to remove all dust or remaining loose particles of old mortar.

New mortar is applied to the joints using one of the many special tools made for such purposes. In general, a long, thin trowel is employed whose blade is from ¼″ to ½″ wide. Some bricklayers wet the joints before applying the new mortar. Before the mortar sets, it should be pointed using a regular pointing tool. Sometimes the mortar is applied with very small trowels so that the new mortar is flush with the bricks and is then brushed with a semi-stiff brush just before it sets. The finishing method is largely a matter of taste. The important item is to force the mortar into the joint so that it completely fills the cavity and sticks in place. Repointing an old wall adds surprising new beauty to it.

Exposed chimneys are apt to need repointing much more frequently than walls. This is because chimneys are alternately hot and cold and because they are generally more exposed to beating rain, wind, and freezing than most walls. It is wise to inspect chimneys, especially near their tops and at the point where they emerge from roofs, every few years. Chimneys which do not have flue linings should be checked yearly and frequently repointed due to their becoming causes for roof fires when mortar joints are loose.

The process of repointing chimneys is the same as explained for walls.

Painting Brickwork. Brickwork may be painted without damage but certainly without improving it any. Whether a wall, for example, is to be painted or not depends entirely upon the owner's taste. When brick walls are painted, there is the additional cost plus maintenance to be considered. Repainting is frequently necessary because painted bricks generally spall, causing unsightly appearance.

There is no appreciable proof that painted brick walls are superior to unpainted walls from the standpoint of insulation beyond the fact that if a wall is painted with a light color and frequently repainted, it will reflect heat.

Bricks which are to be painted should be hard-burned and more resistant to freezing in the presence of moisture than ordinary bricks, in order to prevent spalling and continued unsightly appearance.

In general, well-laid brick walls can be made attractive enough so as not to need painting as a means of adding to their beauty.

Efflorescence. Efflorescence is a light powder or crystallization deposited on the surface of brickwork or concrete and is the result of the evaporation of water carrying water soluble salts. There are two general conditions necessary to produce efflorescence. First, soluble salts present in the wall materials; and second, moisture to carry these salts to the surface of the bricks. In general, good bricks contain but little of the soluble salts which produce efflorescence. The mortars and plasters are more frequently the sources of the salts.

Since moisture is necessary to carry soluble salts to the surface of bricks, efflorescence is evidence that there is faulty construction. Wet walls may be due to defective flashings, gutters, and down-spouts, faulty copings, or improperly filled mortar joints. The use of frozen bricks at the time of construction also adds moisture to walls. Any repairable items should be taken care of, including repointing of the joints.

Efflorescence can be prevented by the use of good materials in proper condition and especially by good workmanship in regard to the proper amounts of mortar in all joints. Unless joints are completely filled, moisture is almost certain to enter walls and very possibly cause efflorescence.

Efflorescence can be removed sometimes by scrubbing the wall with water and a stiff brush. If this treatment is unsuccessful, wet the wall thoroughly with water, then scrub with water containing a 10 per cent solution of muriatic (hydrochloric) acid. Immediately after, the wall should be thoroughly rinsed with plain water. It is sometimes desirable to follow this rinse with water containing approximately 5 per cent of household ammonia.

Cleaning Brickwork.   There are many uncertainties about the cleaning of any brickwork which make the job one for men experienced in the process. Sand blasting frequently is employed as is the steam or steam- and water-jet process.

The sand blasting method actually removes a thin layer from the surface of the bricks. This destroys the original texture of the brick and leaves the surface with a coarse texture which may or may not be pleasing. Also, it is necessary frequently to repoint the joints after sand blasting.

The steam or steam- and hot-water-jet process successfully removes most of the soot and dirt. It is most successful when used for fine-textured, hard-burned bricks.

CHAPTER V

Fireplace Design and Construction

THEORY OF FIREPLACES

Warming Effect. The warming effect of a plain fireplace (one not having special heat distributing features in addition to a modern damper) is considerably less than is generally supposed. There are several reasons for this.

In the first place, warming effect is produced by *radiant* heat from the fire and from the hot back, sides, and hearth surrounding the fire. Heat radiation, like light, travels in straight lines. Unless one is within range of such radiation, little warmth is felt. Even if warmth is felt, it is apparent only on the side of the body which faces the fire. The other side of the body is cold. This fact can be explained more clearly using the example of bright sunshine on an early spring or autumn day when the temperature is low. If a person stands so that the sun's rays are upon him, the side of his body facing the sun will feel some warmth. The side opposite will still feel cold. The same is true in the case of heat radiation from a fireplace. The heat is limited to rather short distances from the fireplace with the result that not all areas, especially in large rooms, are reached by it.

Furthermore, heat from a fireplace is not circulated around the room by air currents. Where rooms are heated by steam radiators, circulation of the air is built up, which carries the heat from the radiator all over the room, gradually raising the room temperature. This does not occur with plain fireplaces.

The foregoing explanation can be visualized more easily by comparing the two sketches shown in Fig. 1. In (A) the heat from the fireplace radiates outward into the room for only a short distance. There is no circulation to warm the air in the room. A person standing or sitting at point X would feel some heat but a person at point Y would feel none at all. In (B) the heat from the radiator circulates completely around the room; all of the air in the room is heated and a person sitting anywhere in the room would feel warmth on all sides of his body.

Still another reason why plain fireplaces provide little real heating is because air from the room in which the fireplace is located flows into the fireplace, through the fire, then up the chimney to the outside. Thus, much of the heat from the fire is carried up the chimney instead of being circulated in the room. As air enters the fireplace, it becomes heated, and because of this rises quickly through the chimney. This

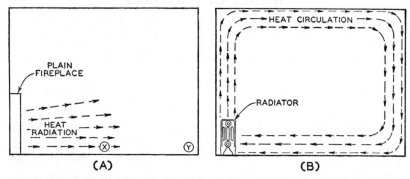

Fig. 1. Heat Radiation from Fireplace (A) and Heat Circulation from a Radiator (B)

causes a suction of air from the room into the fireplace. The air drawn from the room is replaced by outside air which enters the room through cracks around windows and doors. This keeps the air temperature of the room below the comfort level. Tests conducted by the U.S. Bureau of Agricultural Chemistry have shown that approximately five times more air is drawn into a room in this manner than is required for good ventilation. Such excessive ventilation can easily cause chilling drafts. The same tests also have shown that a plain fireplace is only one-third as efficient as a good stove. Nevertheless, plain fireplaces have a place as an auxiliary to a heating plant and for their cheerfulness and charm. In milder climates, a plain fireplace may suffice.

The disadvantages of plain fireplaces can be greatly lessened, however. Casings of heavy metal, provided with heating chambers, heat inlets, and provisions for creating circulation are employed in what are called *modified* fireplaces. These devices make a fireplace much more efficient as a source of heat. Modified fireplaces circulate heat better than stoves, yet retain all the cheerfulness of the plain fireplace.

Aside from the warming effect, one advantage claimed for the modified fireplace is that the correctly designed and proportioned firebox, manufactured with throat, damper, smoke shelf, and chamber, provides a *form* for the masonry, thus reducing the risk of structural failure and assuring a smokeless fireplace. This is a distinct aid to masons,

Unity Is Achieved, although Two Sharply Contrasting Structural
Materials Are Used in This Fireplace
Detroit Building Trades School, Detroit, Michigan

especially if they have not had extensive experience in the design and construction of fireplaces.

Principal Parts of Plain Fireplaces. All principal parts of plain fireplaces are for the most part similar to those of modified fireplaces.

Figs. 2 through 6 inclusive show three typical, plain fireplaces plus some chimney details. These fireplaces are alike in general principles but have some differences in design and construction. By studying these

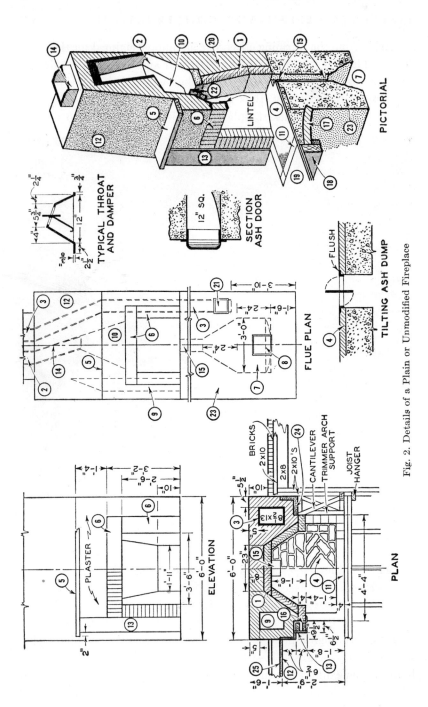

Fig. 2. Details of a Plain or Unmodified Fireplace

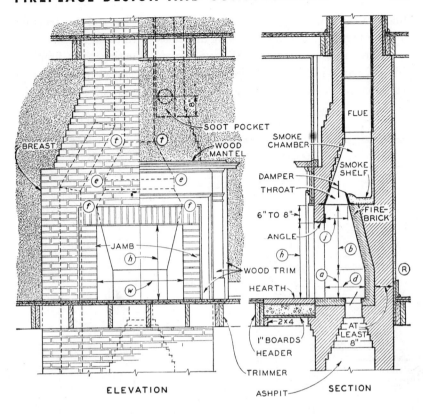

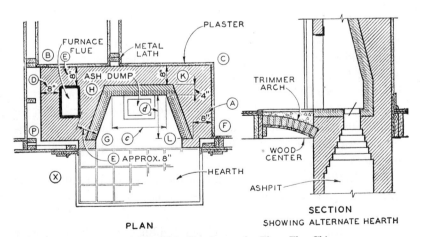

Fig. 3. Details of a Plain Fireplace and a Three-Flue Chimney

illustrations, it will be possible to visualize the design and construction of these fireplaces and the following differences will be observed.

FOOTINGS FOR FIREPLACE FOUNDATIONS. Footings for fireplace chimneys are vital in preventing settlement, and cracks resulting from settlement. The footings in Figs. 4 and 5 are made of concrete; the

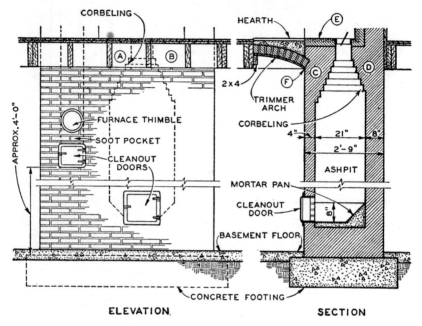

Fig. 4. Details for the Ashpit of the Fireplace Illustrated in Fig. 3.

footing in Fig. 6 is made of brick. Note that the top surfaces of footings should be at a level which coincides with the under surfaces of basement floors.

ASHPITS AND DUMPS. Well-built fireplaces have ashpits and dumps which provide a means of clean and convenient disposal of ashes which accumulate as fuel is consumed. In Fig. 2, the plan, flue plan, and pictorial views show a typical ashpit and dump which are indicated by number *15.*

Note in the plan view of Fig. 2 that the ash dump is located at the back of the hearth, flush with the floor, and next to the rear side of the fireplace. The small detail under the flue plan in the same illustration shows a typical tilting ash dump. The dotted lines in the flue plan show the shape of the ashpit. The shape and location of the ashpit is further illustrated in the pictorial view to be found at the right of Fig. 2. Other typical ashpits and dumps are shown in Figs. 3, 4, 5, and 6. Note that while the shape of these dumps and pits varies somewhat, they are all in the same general position under the fireplace in the chimney.

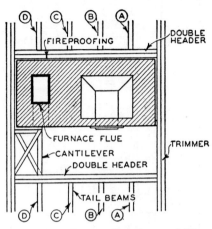

Fig. 5. Joist Framing Details around Fireplace Chimney Shown in Fig. 3

CLEANOUT DOORS. Cleanout doors, as used in ash dumps, make possible the removal of ashes. See Fig. 2 (at *8* in the flue plan) and Figs. 4, 5, and 6. Note the positions and sizes of these doors. Sometimes such doors are called ashpit doors.

Cleanout doors at the bottoms of flues make it possible to remove accumulated soot. Cleanout doors serving this purpose are shown in Fig. 2 (see number *21* in the flue plan) and Figs. 4 and 6. Note that when cleanout doors are used with flues, they should be somewhat wider than the flues they serve.

HEARTHS. In Fig. 2 the hearth is indicated in the plan view by the flagstones and by number *4*. In the pictorial view the hearth is indicated by numbers *4* and *11*. Typical hearths also are shown in the plan and section views of Fig. 3, the section view of Fig. 4, the section view of Fig. 5, and in the section and pictorial views of Fig. 6. The charm or general appearance of a fireplace can be increased considerably by the design and construction of its hearth.

TRIMMER ARCHES. Trimmer arches are construction features which support those portions of the hearth extending beyond the fireplace. A typical trimmer arch is indicated by number *17* in the pictorial view of Fig. 2. This illustration demonstrates how the arch supports the extended portion of the hearth. Other examples of trimmer arches are shown in the section views of Figs. 3, 4, and 5 and in the pictorial and section views of Fig. 6.

JAMBS. Typical jambs are shown in Fig. 2, the elevation view in

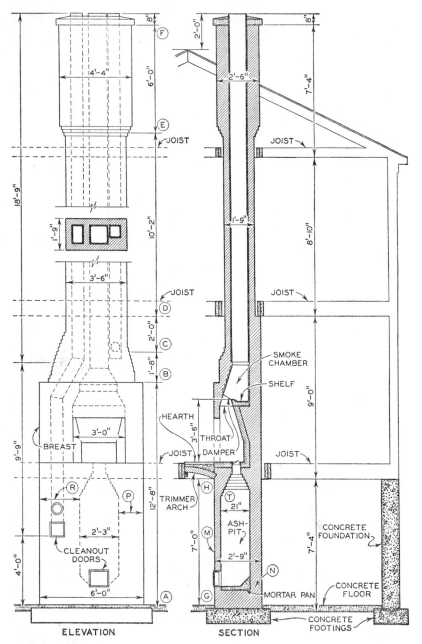

Fig. 6. Elevation and Section Views of the Fireplace and Chimney Shown in Fig. 3

Fig. 3, and in Fig. 6. In Fig. 2 the jambs are indicated by the number *6*. For this particular fireplace, face brick is specified for the jambs. They can be faced also with ornamental tile, stone, or plaster.

Occasionally, as in the case of Figs. 2 and 3, portions of jambs on either side and above the openings are extended about 4″ in order that plaster and wood trim can be carried up to within 8″ of the edge of the openings. This is purely a matter of taste and has no bearing on structural design.

LINTELS. Lintels are for the purpose of supporting the masonry work over the tops of the fireplace openings. The pictorial view in Fig. 2 illustrates the use of the lintel. It is the black symbol indicated by the arrow and is labeled. It can be seen that this lintel supports the weight of the masonry work above it. In the section view at the top of Fig. 3 the lintel is called an angle. Other examples of the lintel may be seen in the section and pictorial views of Fig. 6.

Lintels may be common angle irons, plain steel bars, or curved steel sections. Angles are shown in Figs. 2 and 3 and a curved section in Fig. 6.

THROATS. The throat of a fireplace is the passage through which smoke rises from the hearth or combustion area into the space just below the flue. The upper section view in Fig. 3 shows a typical throat. Others are shown in the section views of Figs. 5 and 6. By studying the flue plan and pictorial views of Fig. 2 it can be seen that the sides of the fireplace at a point just above the lintel gradually slope inward until they finally form the throat. Throats are important features of fireplaces. Unless they are properly designed and constructed, no fireplace will function correctly.

DAMPERS. Dampers regulate the draft and prevent excessive loss of heat through the flues. An ordinary damper (see detail at the right of the flue plan in Fig. 2) consists of a cast-iron frame with a plate hinged so that it may be opened or closed any desired amount. As indicated by number *22* in the pictorial view of Fig. 2, dampers are located in the throats of fireplaces. The upper section view in Fig. 3 and the section views in Figs. 5 and 6 also show typical dampers.

Dampers also prevent loss of heat through fireplace and chimney in winter when the central heating plant is in operation and when the fireplace is not in use.

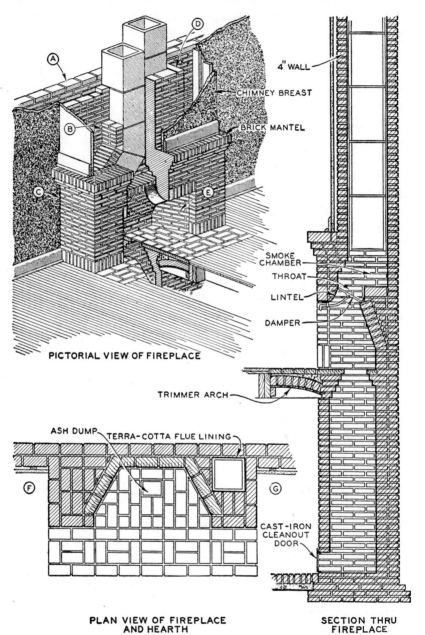

4" WALL

CHIMNEY BREAST

BRICK MANTEL

SMOKE CHAMBER

THROAT

LINTEL

DAMPER

PICTORIAL VIEW OF FIREPLACE

TRIMMER ARCH

ASH DUMP

TERRA-COTTA FLUE LINING

CAST-IRON CLEANOUT DOOR

PLAN VIEW OF FIREPLACE AND HEARTH

SECTION THRU FIREPLACE

Fig. 7. Fireplace and Chimney Built Entirely of Bricks

A roaring pine fire in a fireplace may require the damper to be opened wide. On the other hand, a slow-burning hardwood fire might need but 1″ or 2″ of opening. Such throat adjustments could not be made without the damper. In addition to controlling the speed of burning, dampers prevent flies, mosquitoes, and other insects from entering the house through the chimney in the summer.

SMOKE CHAMBERS AND SHELVES. The smoke chamber is that portion of the fireplace which extends from the top of the throat to the bottom of the flue. Typical examples of the smoke chamber are shown in the pictorial view of Fig. 2 (number *10*), in the upper section of Fig. 3, and in the section views of Figs. 5 and 6. This chamber rapidly collects smoke from the fireplace just prior to the time it rises into the flues.

Smoke shelves prevent down drafts from descending into fireplaces. Without smoke shelves, fireplaces would emit smoke into the rooms in which they are located. Typical examples of smoke shelves are shown in the upper section view of Fig. 3 and in the section view of Fig. 5.

The enlarged detail in Fig. 7 showing the smoke chamber and shelf indicates the paths of smoke and drafts. The dashed line *A* is the path of smoke through the fireplace, through the damper and smoke chamber, and on up the flue. The dashed line *B* indicates down drafts and

shows how they are turned upward by the smoke shelf. In this manner the smoke shelf prevents such drafts from carrying smoke down into the fireplace and at the same time helps to increase the draft up the flue.

FLUES. A thorough discussion of flues is given in Chapter VI on chimneys.

HEADERS. Floor joists must be framed around fireplace chimneys in such a manner as to support the floor safely. Note Fig. 8. It can be seen that joists *A, B,*

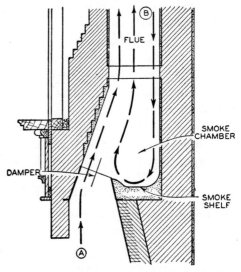

Fig. 8. Section Detail of Fireplace Illustrating the Return of Downdrafts up the Flues

C, and D had to be cut in order to make room for the fireplace chimney. In order to support these joists, the double headers are necessary. This is strictly carpentry work but a mason should understand the use of headers.

The framing shown in Fig. 8 is for the fireplace and chimney illustrated in the plan view of Fig. 3. Notice that the hearth does not extend all the way to the left-hand side of the chimney. Thus, the space marked X in Fig. 3 is framed as indicated by the cantilever in Fig. 8. Headers and cantilever construction also are shown in the plan view of Fig. 2.

MANTELS. Mantels, while not a necessary part of fireplaces, are frequently employed because of their decorative value. As such they add to the charm of a room because of the movable ornaments such as clocks and vases which can be placed upon them. Fig. 9 illustrates two typical fireplaces having mantels. The mantel is shown also at number 5 in the pictorial and elevation views of Fig. 2, in the upper section and elevation views of Fig. 3, and in the section and pictorial views of Fig. 6.

BLANK FLUES. As indicated by number 9 in the plan and flue plan views of Fig. 2, blank flues are occasionally built into fireplace chimneys. The purpose of these flues is to save the cost of the needless material and labor as well as to balance the weight.

FIREPROOFING. As shown in Fig. 8, about 2″ of fireproofing material should be placed between fireplace chimneys and all wooden or inflammable structural members. Even with good masonry work, fireproofing is worth while and should never be omitted.

CHIMNEY BREASTS. Chimney breasts are illustrated in the elevation views of Figs. 3 and 6.

It is possible there are other terms applied to fireplace and chimney parts which enjoy local usage in various sections of the United States. However, the parts which have been named bear standardized terms.

KINDS OF FIREPLACES

Plain Fireplace. The plain fireplace has been explained and illustrated in the foregoing pages. It is the fireplace which has been used to the greatest extent in the past and is still popular where a fireplace is required for its decorative value and only occasional use as an auxiliary source of heat.

Courtesy of American Builder

Fig. 9. Typical Fireplaces Illustrating the Decorative Value of the Mantel
Courtesy of Curtiss Companies Incorporated

Modified Fireplace. When the primary function of a fireplace is to supply heat, the modified fireplace is employed. The principal difference between the two types is the use of a heavy metal casing along with other modifications in the fireplace proper. In addition, provisions are made to insure the circulation of warm air.

Fig. 10 illustrates the details of a typical modified fireplace in a sectioned pictorial drawing. The metal casing composing the fireplace

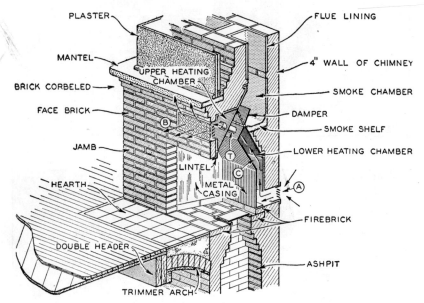

Fig. 10. Details of a Modified Fireplace

proper can be seen. A slightly different presentation which is perhaps more easily visualized is shown in Fig. 11. The basic principle governing the use of such casings is that they absorb and radiate a greater quantity of heat than masonry work. Thus, more heat from the fire is utilized for heating.

The means by which the warm air is circulated is as follows:

Note the lower and upper air chambers near the back of the fireplace and above the lintel in Fig. 10. These chambers are connected by several tubes as shown at T. It is evident that these chambers and tubes are in actual contact with fire and hot smoke. Being metal, they absorb a great deal of heat. As the air in the lower chamber C, the air in the tubes, and the air in the upper chamber becomes heated, it rises and goes out through the heat outlet at B into the room. This upward movement of air through the chambers creates a suction in the lower chamber which draws in cold air from the exterior inlet shown at A. As this incoming air is warmed by heat radiated from the metal walls of the chamber, it rises to the tubes where its temperature is increased by heat radiated from them. The additional heat causes the air to con-

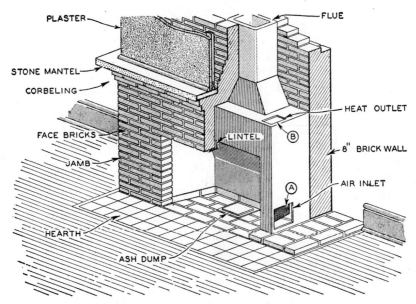

Fig. 11. Another Variety of the Modified Fireplace

tinue its rise until it enters the upper smoke chamber, where its temperature is increased still further with the result that it flows out through the heat outlet into the room. This process, which is continual, circulates heat rather evenly throughout the room in which the fireplace is located.

The fireplace shown in Fig. 11 employs a somewhat different application of the circulation principle explained in the previous paragraph. In this fireplace the air is not taken from the exterior, but through an inlet, A, from the room that is being warmed. The air is warmed as previously explained, rises, and is discharged into the room from outlet B. This process tends to create better circulation of warmed air in the room than when the inlet is located on the exterior. Also, the air leaving the outlet is warmer because, in coming from the room instead of the exterior, it is warmer to start with.

Fig. 12 shows the possible positions for inlets and outlets for a modified fireplace somewhat similar in appearance to the plain fireplace illustrated in Fig. 6. Letters *A*, *B*, *C*, and *D* indicate the possible positions for inlets and outlets if both were desired on the front of the fireplace. Letters *E* and *F* indicate where inlets and outlets could be placed at the ends of such fireplaces. Both inlets and outlets could be placed at either end.

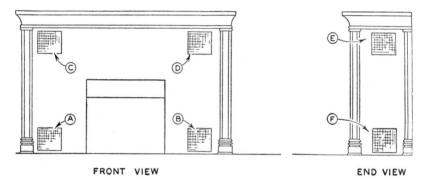

FRONT VIEW   END VIEW

Fig. 12. Possible Positions for Inlets and Outlets in a Modified Fireplace

Fig. 13 shows some of the ways in which ducts (warm air pipes which correspond to outlets) can be run when modified fireplaces are to be used to heat more than one room. The ducts marked *1, 2,* and *3* are for second floor rooms above the fireplace. In such instances, baseboard registers are used. The duct marked *4* shows a possible method of running a cut up into an attic and then to the ceiling of some room a considerable distance from the fireplace. The openings marked *5, 6, 7,* and *8* are outlets such as explained in connection with Fig. 12. The rectangle marked *6* indicates that one central outlet may be used as illustrated in Fig. 10. In any event, no matter what ducts or outlets are used, the inlets near the floor must be employed. For these inlets (*A* and *B* in Fig. 12) a duct must be provided to connect them with the allied openings in the metal casings as shown in Fig. 13.

The metal casings used in modified fireplaces are made by various manufacturers ready for assembly and installation. Each manufac-

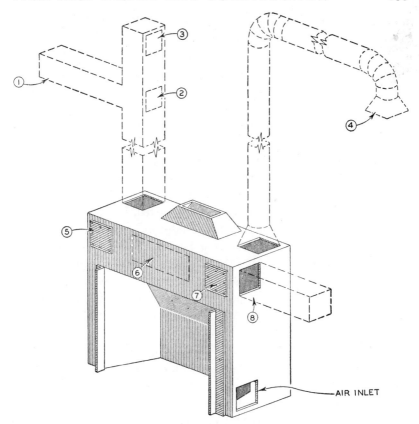

Fig. 13. Possibilities of Ducts Used in Conjunction with Modified Fireplace for Heating Other Rooms

turer's casing is somewhat different, but in general they are quite similar.

FIREPLACE DESIGN

Selection. There are several important points to be considered in the planning of a fireplace before the actual designing can be started. These decisions lead to the actual design.

First, the use of the fireplace must be considered and the question decided as to whether it must serve as a principal source of heat (like a modified fireplace) or merely enhance the appearance of a room where little supplementary heat is required. From the study of the foregoing explanations and illustrations in this chapter, it can be readily understood that the dimensions and some features of design are different for plain and modified fireplaces.

SIZE. There are several significant factors governing the sizes of fireplaces which will be considered in order of their importance.

General Considerations. Thirty inches is a practical height for any fireplace if the width of the opening is less than 6 feet. Openings approximately 30″ to 36″ wide are usually made with square corners. The higher the opening is made, the greater the chance for a smoky chimney. In general, the wider the fireplace opening, the greater should be the depth. A shallow fireplace will throw more heat but requires smaller pieces of fuel. In small fireplaces, a depth of 12″ will permit good draft if the throat is properly constructed. However, a depth of from 16″ to 18″ is recommended especially as a means of preventing brands from falling out on the floor beyond the hearth. Second floor fireplaces are as a rule smaller than fireplaces located on the first floor. This is true because the chimney width need not be as wide and because the flue height is less than for first floor fireplaces.

Brick fireplaces and their chimneys are in general smaller than those built of stone. This is because of the added wall thicknesses required in connection with the use of stone. A brick fireplace can generally be built quicker and at less cost than one built of stone.

Widths of Openings. The type of fuel to be burned is an important consideration and should be decided upon early in the planning stage. For example, if cordwood (4′0″ long) is cut in half, a 30″ wide fireplace opening is sufficient. If coal is to be burned, a fireplace opening of less width will be satisfactory. Figs. 9, 14, and 15 show fireplaces having openings of approximately 30″ width. Fireplaces having an opening from 30″ to 36″ generally are suitable for rooms having floor areas up to 400 square feet. Larger rooms should have proportionately larger fireplaces. This general rule applies to both plain and modified fireplaces.

Typical widths for fireplace openings are shown in the first column of Table I. For example, the widths of the openings (see *w* in the plan view of Fig. 3) run all the way from 24″ to 72 inches.

Heights of Openings. In the second column of Table I are shown the recommended heights (see *h* in the top section view of Fig. 3) for various widths of openings. For example, an opening 30″ wide should be

Fig. 14. Modern Treatment of Fireplace in Which Mantel Has Been Omitted

Courtesy of American Builder

Fig. 15. Fireplace with Traditional Styling Given Modern Touch by Painting

Courtesy of American Builder

TABLE I. RECOMMENDED DIMENSIONS IN INCHES FOR PLAIN FIREPLACES*

OPENING		DEPTH, d	MINIMUM BACK (HORIZONTAL) c	VERTICAL BACK WALL, a	INCLINED BACK WALL, b	OUTSIDE DIMENSIONS OF STANDARD RECTANGULAR FLUE LINING	INSIDE DIAMETER OF STANDARD ROUND FLUE LINING
Width, w	Height, h						
24	24	16–18	14	14	16	8½ x 8½	10
28	24	16–18	14	14	16	8½ x 8½	10
24	28	16–18	14	14	20	8½ x 8½	10
30	28	16–18	16	14	20	8½ x 13	10
36	28	16–18	22	14	20	8½ x 13	12
42	28	16–18	28	14	20	8½ x 18	12
36	32	18–20	20	14	24	8½ x 18	12
42	32	18–20	26	14	24	13 x 13	12
48	32	18–20	32	14	24	13 x 13	15
42	36	18–20	26	14	28	13 x 13	15
48	36	18–20	32	14	28	13 x 18	15
54	36	18–20	38	14	28	13 x 18	15
60	36	18–20	44	14	28	13 x 18	15
42	40	20–22	24	17	29	13 x 13	15
48	40	20–22	30	17	29	13 x 18	15
54	40	20–22	36	17	29	13 x 18	15
60	40	20–22	42	17	29	18 x 18	18
66	40	20–22	48	17	29	18 x 18	18
72	40	22–28	51	17	29	18 x 18	18

*Letters at heads of columns refer to Fig. 3.

28″ high. Note that the opening height is taken as the distance from the hearth to the lintel.

Depths of Openings. The third column of Table I shows the recommended depths for fireplaces (see *d* in the upper section view of Fig. 3) having openings of various widths and heights. For example, a fireplace having on opening 30″ wide and 28″ high should have a depth of at least 16″ to 18 inches.

Back Widths. In the fourth column of Table I are shown the recommended minimum back widths (horizontal) (see *c* in the plan view of Fig. 3) for fireplaces having certain other dimensions. For example, when a fireplace opening is 30″ in width, 28″ high, and 16″ to 18″ deep, the horizontal back width should be at least 16 inches.

Back Heights. The fifth column of Table I gives the recommended heights for vertical backs (see *a* in the top section view of Fig. 3) for fireplaces having certain other interior and opening dimensions. A fireplace having an opening 30″ wide, an opening height of 28″, a depth of 16″ to 18″, and a horizontal back dimension of 16″, should have a vertical back dimension 14″ in height.

In like manner, the height of the inclined backs (see *b* in the top section view of Fig. 3) for chimneys is shown in the sixth column of

Table I. The height of the inclined back for the chimney under discussion is shown to be 20 inches.

RECTANGULAR FLUE SIZES. From column 7 of Table I the recommended flue size for the 30″ width fireplace is seen to be 8½″ x 13 inches. Or, as is demonstrated in Chapter VI, the cross-sectional area of a fireplace flue should be equal to $\frac{1}{12}$ the area of the fireplace opening. If a fireplace opening is 30″ wide and 28″ high, its area is 30 x 28, or 840 square inches. Standard sizes of flue lining sometimes do not have a cross-sectional area which exactly matches the fireplace opening area in the ratio just indicated. In such a case, a flue size having an area slightly in excess of $\frac{1}{12}$ the area of the fireplace opening is proper.

ROUND FLUE SIZES. Column 8 in Table I shows recommended round flue sizes for fireplaces having certain dimensions.

THROATS AND DAMPERS. At j, in the upper section of Fig. 3, is shown the throat. Correct throat construction contributes more to the efficiency of a fireplace than any other single feature except the flues. There must be a constriction at the throat in order to maintain good drafts. The cross-sectional area of the throat should not be less than the cross-sectional area of the flue. Their length should be equal to the width of the fireplace opening. The sides of the fireplace should be vertical up to the throat opening (see ff in the elevation view of Fig. 3). Throats (see upper section view in Fig. 3) should be set 6″ to 8″ above lintels and should not be more than 4″ to 6″ wide. Starting 5″ above the throat (see ee in the elevation view of Fig. 3), the sides should be drawn in at tt to equal the flue area. If dampers are installed (see typical damper illustrated at left of pictorial drawing in Fig. 2) the widths of the openings at the throats will depend upon the frames of the dampers—the width of the throat being regulated by the hinged covers of the dampers. If dampers are omitted, the openings should not be more than 4 inches.

Manufacturers of fireplace equipment can supply catalogues and other information in which they specify sizes of throats and dampers for various sizes of fireplaces. They will always assist any mason in selecting proper dampers and throat sizes for any given fireplace.

SMOKE SHELVES AND CHAMBERS. Smoke shelves are made by setting the brickwork back at the tops of throats to the lines of flue walls for the full lengths of throats. Their depth may vary from 6″ to 12″ or more, depending on the depth of the fireplace.

Smoke chambers constitute the spaces extending from the tops of throats (see *ee* in the elevation view of Fig. 3) up to the bottom of the flue proper (*tt*) and between the side walls. The walls should be drawn inward 30° from the vertical after the tops of the throats (*ee*) are passed and smoothly plastered with cement mortar not less than ½″ in thickness.

LINTELS. Lintels of 3½″ x 3½″ x ¼″ angles, or ½″ x 3″ x 6″ flat or curved bars, are generally used for fireplaces having openings not greater than 4 feet.

JAMBS. For fireplace openings up to 36″ in width, the jambs should be from 12″ to 16″ or more, depending on whether flues from below the fireplace must be carried in the same chimneys. Note the plan view in Fig. 3. On the right-hand side where there is no flue, the jamb is approximately 12″ wide. Because of the flue on the other side, the jamb is approximately 20 inches. In Fig. 6 the jambs are approximately 16″ wide.

MANTELS. The design of mantels, if they are to be used, is purely one of taste. Brick mantels such as shown in Fig. 6 are attractive, especially when the jambs of the fireplace are entirely visible and faced with brick. When wood mantels similar to the one shown in Fig. 2 are desired, they and the wood trim to accompany them can be purchased ready to install from woodworking mills. For example, the two fireplaces shown in Fig. 9 have wood mantels. The mantels and the wood trim that goes with them are purchased complete and ready to assemble and install. Stone mantels such as shown in Fig. 11 can be purchased ready to install or can be made at any stone supply yard.

ASHPITS AND DUMPS. Ash dumps (see detail in Fig. 2 of tilting ash dump) are usually 3″ x 8″ with the long dimension parallel to the back of the fireplace. However, any other dimensions, the total of which is about the same as the recommended 3″ x 8″, are satisfactory. The door should be constructed so that it will tilt and should be flush with the hearth. These doors can be purchased in various shapes ready to install from fireplace parts manufacturers.

Ashpits, as shown in Figs. 4, 5, and 6, should be large as a means of avoiding clogging and in order to save on the use of brick and mortar. The width should be about 2'3" and the thickness about 21" when used in conjunction with fireplace openings having widths up to 42" and depths up to 18 inches. For larger fireplaces, the pit dimensions should be slightly greater. Whatever size pit is used, the wall marked *M* in the section view of Fig. 5 should never be less than 4" and the widths, marked *R* and *P* in the elevation view, not less than 16 inches.

The tops of ashpits can be corbeled starting at the hearth level as shown in the section view of Fig. 6 or somewhat below the hearth as shown in the section view of Fig. 4.

At the bottoms of ashpits it is a good policy to build up a mortar pan as shown in the section views of Figs. 4 and 5. This facilitates the removal of the ashes. However, if desired, the bottoms of the ashpits can be left flat as shown in the section view of Fig. 6.

CLEANOUT DOORS. These metal doors are purchased from fireplace parts manufacturers and are ready to install as the masonry work is laid up. They can be purchased in various sizes to fit any requirement —flue bottoms, ashpits, etc.

FIREPLACE LININGS. The firebrick for fireplace linings should be laid up so as to make the lining a full 4" in thickness. In other words, the firebrick should be laid flat and not on edge. When laid flat with the long side exposed, there is less danger of their falling out of the wall. It is best to lay firebrick in fire clay mortar. The sides, vertical backs, and inclined backs should all have such a lining.

Firebrick. This material is a type of brick which is especially made to withstand contact with heat. Ordinary brick do not have this quality to the extent to permit their use in place of firebrick. This is an important point to remember in the construction of fireplaces. Typical brick fireplace linings are shown in the plan and pictorial views of Fig. 2.

TRIMMER ARCHES. As indicated in the two section views of Fig. 3, there are two methods of handling the design of the trimmer arch. In the upper section view, the arch is really flat and is supported at the fireplace end by corbeling and at the header end by a 2 x 4 block. About 5" of concrete is poured and the hearth surfacing laid on the concrete. Perhaps the most common trimmer arch is the one shown in the lower section view of Fig. 3. The arch is laid up using brick which are supported at the fireplace end by being recessed into the ashpit wall. They are supported at the other end by the header. Concrete is poured as explained for the flat arch. The illustration shows the position of the arch. The length of such arches depends on the hearth dimensions.

HEARTHS. The hearth should be flush with the floor of the room the fireplace is in. They should project at least 16″ from the jambs and should be of brick, stone, terra cotta, tile, or any other fireproof material. Their thickness, including the trimmer arch, should be not less than 5 inches. The length of the hearth should not be less than the width of the fireplace opening plus 16 inches.

EXTERIOR FINISH OF FIREPLACES. The selection of exterior finish is a matter to be decided upon after a study has been made of the surrounding trim and ornamentation. For example, in recreation rooms, a fireplace such as shown in Fig. 6 might be used. Fireplaces such as those shown in Figs. 2, 9, 14, and 15 are more suitable for living and dining rooms. Examples of fireplace exterior finish can be obtained from woodworking mills, fireplace parts manufacturers, and current household magazines.

EXTERIOR CHIMNEY SHAPES. The shapes of exterior fireplace chimneys generally change above the second floor level or at points somewhat below that level, since only a width large enough to house the flues is necessary above the fireplace. The elevation view of Fig. 3 illustrates this point.

INTERIOR CHIMNEY SHAPES. The shapes of interior chimneys also change at or just below the second floor level. Note in Fig. 6 that the point designated by letter A in the pictorial sketch is almost at the second floor level. The chimney at B is already much narrower than that at C. The other side of the chimney has likewise been narrowed so that width DB is just enough to house properly the two flues. By making the chimneys just wide enough to house the flues, once they have been built up above the smoke chambers, a great saving in material is achieved as well as the saving in space in second floor rooms.

CHIMNEY WIDTHS AND THICKNESSES. In this discussion the width of a fireplace chimney is taken as the distance BC in the plan view of Fig. 3 or as indicated by the 6′0″ dimension near the bottom of the chimney in Fig. 5.

Brick Chimneys. The width of a fireplace chimney from the foundation to a point somewhere above the fireplace must be wide enough to include the fireplace, one or more flues, and ample chimney walls. If Fig. 5 is carefully studied it will be seen that the width of the chimney between points *A* and *B* is greater than at any point above *B.*

There is no standard theory about chimney widths just above and below fireplaces except that they should have pleasing proportions and should be strong and firesafe. Study the plan view in Fig. 3. Here, the fireplace, one flue, and the chimney walls make up the entire width. Note that distances *A, D,* and *E* are 8 inches. Walls of this thickness are recommended over the thinner walls shown in the plan views of Figs. 2 and 6. The walls shown in Fig. 2 are only 4″ thick. While they are not unsafe, they require considerable brick cutting and laborious construction. The walls shown in the plan view of Fig. 6 are probably safe and strong and require little cutting of brick. However, the walls between the flue and the fireplace surface and between the flue and the surface of the exterior of the chimney are just one brick width or 4″ in thickness. This is much thinner than recommended in terms of safety from fire.

In Fig. 5 note the thickness of the fireplace chimney between points *G* and *H* in the section view. This thickness is indicated by the 2′9″ dimension shown near the base of the fireplace. The thickness of a fireplace chimney must be sufficient to include the fireplace and at least 8″ of masonry work between the rear face of the fireplace and the exterior face of the chimney. The plan view of Fig. 6 shows 8″ of masonry which just meets the requirements of the rule. In the plan view of Fig. 3 a thickness of 8″ plus another 4″ is shown. This constitutes a much better type of construction which is superior in every respect and increases fire protection immeasurably.

METAL FIREPLACE CASINGS. The metal casings for modified fireplaces can be purchased ready to assemble and install from various manufacturers. Most of these manufacturers have a range of sizes from which selections can be made to fit the needs of the rooms to be heated. All of them will supply free catalogues, sales service, and instruction sheets or manuals relative to the proper selection and installation of their casings.

As shown in Figs. 10 and 11, the metal cases are surrounded by masonry work. This means that definite dimensions must be followed in designing the openings, jambs, walls, ashpits, etc., in order that the casings can be set into place at the proper time during construction and the masonry work laid up around and above them. All such dimensions are given in the manufacturer's catalogues in somewhat the same manner as the dimensions for plain fireplaces.

DESIGNING PLAIN AND MODIFIED FIREPLACES

Design Procedure for Plain Fireplaces. As a general rule, the mason will seldom be called upon to design the fireplace he builds. However, changes in building plans to include a fireplace and other such exceptions make this knowledge essential. In addition, a more complete understanding of the problems involved in building the fireplace will be possible if it is known how they are planned or designed. The recommended procedure for building a plain fireplace similar to the ones shown in Figs. 3, 4, and 5 is as follows:

1. Based on the floor area of the room in which the fireplace is to be located, select the opening size and other related dimensions from columns 1 through 6 in Table I.
2. Make a scale drawing showing the plan arrangement of the fireplace similar to *GHKL* in Fig. 3. Remember that the back of the fireplace is considerably narrower than the opening width as indicated by the difference between the dimensions in columns 1 and 4 of Table I.
3. Draw in the lines representing the firebrick fireplace lining and a second set at least 8″ beyond. These lines represent the back of the chimney (*BC* in the plan view of Fig. 3). This line can be made any length at this stage since it is just a means of locating the chimney back.
4. Next, the furnace flue is drawn in. In the best types of construction, this flue is at least 8″ from the back of the chimney and is not nearer than 8″ to the side of the fireplace.
5. Draw a line such as *PG* in the plan view of Fig. 3, representing the left-hand jamb and breast. Following this, a line is drawn which represents the left-hand end of the chimney such as line *PB* in Fig. 3. This line must not be nearer than 8″ to the furnace flue.
Note: Flues can be nearer than 8″ to the sides and backs of fireplaces but this practice is not recommended when the 8″ distance is possible. An example of a flue which does not adhere to this recommendation is shown in Fig. 6.
6. Draw the jamb and end of the chimney on the right side, making the end at least 8″ from the firebrick lining.
7. Check the over-all dimensions to make certain that whole bricks can be laid up without any cutting being necessary. Such planning is shown to good advantage in the plan view of Fig. 6. In the event whole bricks cannot be

used, the dimensions may have to be changed a bit in order to accomplish this.

8. Following this, the hearth is drawn in, and the ash dump and projecting jambs located.

9. Next, make a section drawing of the fireplace according to dimensions *h, d, a,* and *b* from Table I, similar to the upper section view in Fig. 3 and the section view in Fig. 5.

10. Draw in the ashpit and foundation, and the trimmer arch.

11. Draw in the throat using the dimensions of the damper selected. Draw in the smoke chamber and shelf following the directions given relative to *ff, ee,* and *tt* in connection with the elevation view of Fig. 3.

12. Draw an elevation view of the fireplace and chimney and show the flues by means of dashed lines.

13. Check over all three drawings to make certain that all parts of each correspond exactly with the same parts in the other drawings.

14. Draw in the dimensions of all parts in all three sketches and make sure they check accurately against one another.

Design Procedure for Modified Fireplaces. The methods involved in designing modified fireplaces are the same as described for plain fireplaces except that dimensions and other special instructions must be taken from manufacturers' instruction sheets and/or manuals.

Drawings such as those just described are a necessity when designing a fireplace. They will aid in avoiding errors and faulty design and act as a guide during the actual construction.

FIREPLACE CONSTRUCTION

If fireplaces and their accompanying chimneys are parts of residences or other small buildings which have been designed by architects, most of the necessary detail drawings will be shown in the working drawings. These details, which are parts of plan, elevation, and section drawings, usually show the principal dimensions for fireplaces and chimneys as well as their exact locations in the buildings of which they are a part. The architect's written specifications also describe such items as dampers, trimmer arches, ash dumps, and the other fireplace components. However, architect's drawings sometimes do not show the exact details pertaining to such features as smoke chambers and shelves, corbeling, and other important fireplace components. In such cases the mason must rely on his knowledge of fireplace construction in order to obtain satisfactory results in building them. The foregoing parts of this chapter have been aimed at helping inexperienced masons to acquire such knowledge.

In plans which have been drawn by architects, the exact locations of fireplace chimneys are shown in all floor plan drawings including the basement. The mason studies these plans and determines from them the exact place to start construction. If the mason must work without architect's plans or if such plans are inadequate in the presentation of information concerning the fireplace and chimney, he must make his own sketches showing the fireplace and chimney size and location, and their relation to the various floors, walls, and roof in the building of which they are to be a part. Such drawings are a great aid from the standpoint of construction and are the means of preventing mistakes in the masonry work.

Building Ashpits. After the footings have been laid it is a good idea to allow at least three days during warm weather and at least a week during cold weather before starting the construction of ashpits.

The first step is to draw the outline of the ashpit. The outside dimensions are laid out on the surface of the footing with chalk or a pencil having heavy lead. This location is then checked by the use of plumb bobs to make certain the outline places the bottom of the ashpit so that when the walls of the chimney are built up, they will be in exactly the right position in relation to headers which the carpenters have prepared at the first floor level (see Fig. 8).

Bricks are laid without mortar around the outline of the ashpit as a means of determining the number of whole bricks which can be used and how much, if any, cutting of bricks will be necessary. The bricks are then pushed aside and mortar is spread on the surface of the footing around the outlines. Common bricks are used entirely for interior chimneys. Face bricks should be used for exterior chimneys wherever the chimney surface is visible from the outside. The bricks should be well bedded in the mortar, keeping them well within the outlines. The ends of the bricks should be carefully buttered to make certain the vertical joints will be good. It should be remembered that $\frac{1}{4}''$ to $\frac{3}{8}''$ joints make stronger masonry work than do larger joints. Once the first course has been laid, mortar is spread on the top surface of the bricks and the second course started. The joints should be staggered as shown in Fig. 4 in the elevation view.

When four or five courses have been laid, the ashpit door frame should be placed in position as shown in Figs. 2 and 4. Five or six

Tooling Joints in Wall Laid in Old English Bond

This bond is produced by alternating a course of stretchers with a course of headers.
A queen closure is laid next to the corner bricks in every course of headers.

Detroit Building Trades School, Detroit, Michigan

Round Jointer Used to Shape Mortar Joints

Jointers are of various shapes and form a necessary part of the bricklayer's equipment.

Detroit Building Trades School, Detroit, Michigan

additional courses are then laid so that there is at least one course above the door frame.

Beginning at a level flush with the bottom of the ashpit door, the ashpit walls (*M*, *N*, *R*, and *P* in Fig. 5) are started. Such walls vary in thickness from one to three brick widths. For example, wall *M* in Fig. 5 is one brick width in thickness, or 4 inches. Fig. 16 at (A) shows a horizontal section of the chimney pictured in Figs. 4 and 5. This section was taken at the ashpit door and the walls have been marked to correspond with the same walls in Fig. 5.

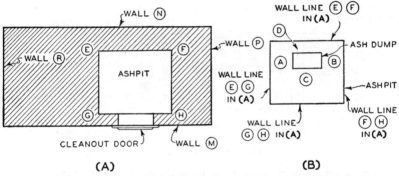

Fig. 16. Horizontal Section View of Chimney Shown in Fig. 6 Illustrating Ashpit Door (A), and Position of Ash Dump (B)

The laying of the ashpit walls continues, including the placing of the cleanout door for the flue soot pocket and the furnace thimble. These two features of the ashpit wall are built in just as was described for the ashpit door. At a point 18″ to 24″ below the first-floor levels such as at *T* in the section view of Fig. 5, corbeling should be started as a means of narrowing the ashpit sides to the dimensions of the ash dumps. Fig. 16 at (B) shows the outline of the ashpit as well as the ash dump. The interior faces of walls *GE*, *EF*, *FH*, and *HG* in (A) of Fig. 16 and noted in (B) of Fig. 16 must be gradually corbeled out over the distances *A*, *D*, *B*, and *C* (see [B] of Fig. 16) until they form the ash dump opening. This corbeling is shown at *A*, *D*, *B*, and *C* in Fig. 4. The amount each of the courses must be corbeled out and the number of courses to be corbeled must be determined on the basis of the size of the ash dumps and the wall thicknesses. Typical corbeling is visible in Fig. 6 in the section view and in the pictorial view at the cutaway part of the pictorial section just below the hearth.

Building Fireplace Floors.　The parts of hearths which comprise fireplace floors (see *E* in the section view of Fig. 4) should be made of one layer of firebrick laid flat. Care should be taken to see that such floors are perfectly level and that the ash dumps are flush with them. Sometimes the bricks around the dumps must be chipped in order that the dumps will be flush with the floors.

Building Trimmer Arches.　Trimmer arches shown in Figs. 4, 5, and 6 are constructed of bricks, boards, wood blocks, wood center forms, and concrete.

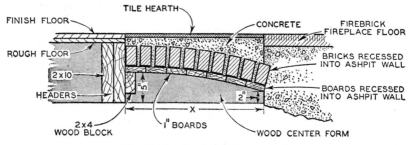

Fig. 17. Details of the Trimmer Arch

When ashpit walls have been built up to the level of the fireplace floors, the trimmer arches can be made. These arches extend under the hearths for the full length of the hearths.

Note the wood center form in Fig. 17. These should be spaced not more than 2′0″ apart under the arch. Their length, *X*, is governed by the width of the hearth. They are usually 5″ or 6″ high at the end furthest from the fireplace and about 2″ high where they are recessed into the ashpit walls. Any curvature is satisfactory as long as the concrete can be twice as thick at the ashpit walls as it is at the headers. Wood boards approximately an inch in thickness are nailed to the curved or top edges of these center forms as shown in Fig. 17. The blocking is made of 2 x 4's, 3 x 3's, etc.

When the wood center forms are in place, about half an inch of mortar of the same mix used for ashpit walls should be spread over the boards and the bricks laid, one row at a time, starting at the recess in the ashpit walls. Care should be taken to have mortar in all vertical joints. The joints should not be greater than ⅜″, and should be staggered in alternate rows.

When all bricks have been laid, stiff concrete should be placed using a 1:2:4 mix, taking care that it is carefully tamped. The top surface of the concrete should be perfectly level and half an inch or more below the surface of the finished floor surfaces, depending on what hearth surfacing is to be employed.

If bricks are used for hearth surfacing, their color, the color of the mortar, and the pattern in which the bricks are laid are worked out following the architect's designs or personal taste. If tile surfaces are required, tile setters should do that portion of the work.

The wood center forms are left in place as permanent construction.

Building Fireplaces. After the fireplace floors and trimmer arches have been completed, the jambs, end walls, fireplace side walls, and back walls are laid up. Fig. 6 shows a typical arrangement of bricks for such walls. The jambs, end walls (F and G), the fireplace side walls (E), and the vertical back wall should all be laid up at the same time, course by course. The side walls and vertical back walls are laid with firebrick. The inclined portion of the back wall is also laid course by course with the other sections so as to be supported by the side walls.

Lintels should be placed when the jambs are up to the maximum opening height, as in Fig. 3. Each end of the lintel should have a bearing of at least 3 inches. The inclined back walls are laid up to the required heights (b in Fig. 3) while at the same time continuing the laying of the rear walls back of the smoke chambers. The smoke shelves are made of mortar in such a way that they have a curved or dished surface. The size of the throat depends on the damper to be used.

Study the pictorial section of Fig. 6 and the dotted lines from ff to ee to tt in the elevation view of Fig. 3 to see how smoke chambers are formed above throats and how these chambers gradually are reduced in size and shape to form flue dimensions.

Brick or stone mantels, as pictured in Figs. 6 and 10, are easily installed as shown in those illustrations. Wood mantels and any surrounding woodwork are installed by carpenters.

The building of modified fireplaces and their chimneys is exactly the same as has been explained for plain fireplaces except that the metal cases support some of the masonry work and that some of the masonry work is laid up around the casings and their various heat ducts and registers.

ESTIMATING

The method involved in estimating the number of bricks required for fireplaces and chimneys is explained here because so many inexperienced masons require a knowledge of the procedure.

The fireplace and chimney illustrated in Fig. 5 are used as an example. In Fig. 5, two sets of dimensions are given. There are those which refer to the *approximate* sizes of the voids or openings. All others refer to the outside dimensions of the masonry work. The letters *A* to *F* in the elevation indicate sections used in estimating the quantities of brick required.

A convenient method for estimating the number of bricks in fireplace chimneys is to calculate the volume of the various sections which differ in outside dimensions and then subtract the voids or hollow spaces which constitute the ashpits, fireplaces, flues, etc. This will be the total cubic feet of brickwork which, when multiplied by 22.5, is converted to the number of bricks required. For ease in making calculations, inches and fractions of an inch can be converted to feet by multiplying by 0.0833. In Fig. 5, most dimensions are in thirds of a foot or quarters of a foot. In such cases it is simpler to express the dimension in decimals. For example, 12'8" (height *AB* in the elevation of Fig. 5) becomes 12.66 feet since 8" equals two-thirds of a foot. In estimating the number of bricks for any fireplace and chimney it should be remembered that the answer will be a *close approximation*. For this reason it is not necessary to provide dimensions for each section of the chimney and fireplace. For example, the corbeled section *BC* in the elevation view has no width dimension. However, it is close enough in width to the section *EF* for the purposes of the problem. Therefore, this dimension is used.

1. The first step is to estimate the total volume of masonry by multiplying together the width, depth, and height of the various sections of fireplace and chimney pictured in Fig. 5.

Section	Width (Feet)		Depth (Feet)		Height (Feet)		Volume (Cubic Feet)
AB	6.0	×	2.75	×	12.66	=	208.89
BC	4.25	×	2.5	×	1.66	=	17.60
CD	3.5	×	2.0	×	2.0	=	14.00
DE	3.5	×	1.75	×	10.16	=	62.20
EF	4.33	×	2.5	×	6.0	=	65.00
					Total volume		367.7

2. Next, estimate the total volume of the voids by multiplying together their width, depth, and height.

Section	Width (Feet)		Depth (Feet)		Height (Feet)		Volume (Cubic Feet)
Ashpit	2.33	×	1.5	×	7.0	=	24.46
Fireplace	3.0	×	1.5	×	3.5	=	15.75
Smoke chamber	2.0	×	1.16	×	2.0	=	4.64
8½″ x 13″ flue	.76	sq. ft.		×	28.5	=	21.66
13″ x 13″ flue	1.17	sq. ft.		×	18.75	=	21.93
8½″ x 13″ flue	.50	sq. ft.		×	18.75	=	9.37

Total volume of voids 97.81

3. Subtract the volume of the voids from the total volume of the masonry.

$$367.7$$
$$-97.8$$
Net volume, therefore, 269.9

4. Multiply the net volume of masonry by the number of bricks per cubic foot.

$$269.9$$
$$\times 22.5$$
$$6,072.75$$

The number of bricks required to lay the fireplace and chimney pictured in Fig. 5 will be 6,072, or 6.1 thousand bricks.

To estimate the mortar needed to lay the fireplace and chimney shown in Fig. 5, multiply the mortar material (which will give a 1:1:6 mix for 1,000 bricks) in the following by 6.1.

Bags, hydrated lime. . . . . 2.6 × 6.1 = 16 bags
Sacks, Portland cement. . . . . 3.5 × 6.1 = 22 sacks
Sand, cubic feet. . . . . 18.0 × 6.1 = 110 cubic feet

Other materials which will be needed to construct this fireplace and chimney include:

One each, 6″ and 8″ thimble
28′ of 8½″ x 13″ flue lining
20′ of 13″ x 13″ flue lining
20′ of 8½″ x 8½″ flue lining

One damper
Two cleanout doors
One ash dump
One mantel

CHAPTER VI

Chimneys and Fireplace Construction

Chimney Components. Fig. 1 shows a pictorial view of a typical chimney. It extends from the basement of the residence up to and beyond the roof. Fig. 2 illustrates the plan, elevation, and section views of the same chimney. If these drawings are studied carefully, the principal parts of the typical chimney can be learned. This particular chimney was designed to serve a fireplace, furnace, and gas water heater. The elevation and section views show the fireplace at the first floor level. The elevation view shows the intakes or openings for pipes from the furnace and water heater in the basement. It also shows the ashpit and the ash cleanout doors in the basement for the fireplace. Note that in the elevation view there are parallel vertical lines composed of short dashes which extend over the furnace and water heater intakes and above the fireplace. These are the flues which carry off the fumes and the gases. In the section view, the fireplace flue between the top of the fireplace and the top of the chimney is shown by a solid line.

The plan view in Fig. 2 shows flues which are marked *1, 2,* and *3.* These numbers correspond to the same numbers in the elevation view.

The flues are surrounded with brickwork which is called the chimney walls. These walls hold the flues in place and constitute the structural work of the chimney. The entire chimney is supported by a concrete footing which is necessary to prevent settlement and cracks.

DRAFT. A draft accomplishes two objectives. First, it carries away the fumes and gases. Second, and more important, it provides a constant supply of fresh air which is necessary to keep fires burning at proper rates. The draft is created as the hot fumes and gases, which are lighter than air, seek a higher level. They rise from the fireplace or furnace into the flues. The higher they go, the faster their rate of ascent becomes. This column of rising gas and heated air causes a

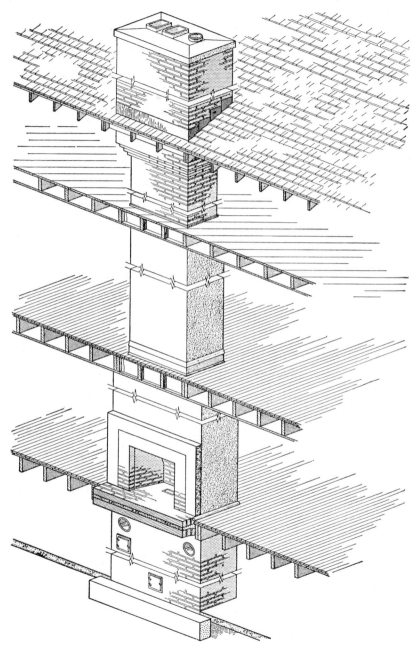

Fig. 1. Pictorial View of a Three-Flue Chimney with Fireplace

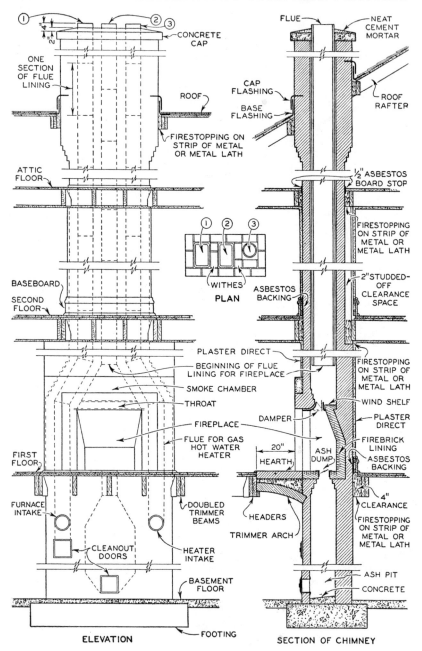

ELEVATION

- ① ② ③
- CONCRETE CAP
- ONE SECTION OF FLUE LINING
- ROOF
- ATTIC FLOOR
- BASEBOARD
- SECOND FLOOR
- FIRESTOPPING ON STRIP OF METAL OR METAL LATH
- WITHES
- **PLAN**
- ① ② ③
- ASBESTOS BACKING
- PLASTER DIRECT
- BEGINNING OF FLUE LINING FOR FIREPLACE
- SMOKE CHAMBER
- THROAT
- FIREPLACE
- FLUE FOR GAS HOT WATER HEATER
- FIRST FLOOR
- FURNACE INTAKE
- CLEANOUT DOORS
- DOUBLED TRIMMER BEAMS
- HEATER INTAKE
- BASEMENT FLOOR
- FOOTING

SECTION OF CHIMNEY

- FLUE
- NEAT CEMENT MORTAR
- CAP FLASHING
- BASE FLASHING
- ROOF RAFTER
- ½" ASBESTOS BOARD STOP
- FIRESTOPPING ON STRIP OF METAL OR METAL LATH
- 2" STUDDED-OFF CLEARANCE SPACE
- FIRESTOPPING ON STRIP OF METAL OR METAL LATH
- WIND SHELF
- PLASTER DIRECT
- DAMPER
- FIREBRICK LINING
- ASH DUMP
- ASBESTOS BACKING
- 20"
- HEARTH
- HEADERS
- TRIMMER ARCH
- 4" CLEARANCE
- FIRESTOPPING ON STRIP OF METAL OR METAL LATH
- ASH PIT
- CONCRETE

Fig. 2. Elevation and Sectional Views of Chimney Shown in Fig. 1

suction at the bottom of the fireplace or furnace. This suction causes air to be drawn through the fuel beds in the fireplace or furnace which in turn makes the fire burn at the desired rate. For this reason, chimneys must have certain minimum heights. Factors governing these minimum heights are discussed more fully in the pages that follow.

FLUES. Chimney flues can be formed of the bricks or other material which has been used for the chimney walls as shown in Fig. 3. Flues also can be lined with rectangular or round flue linings of fire clay as illustrated in Fig. 4.

A chimney which has been erected without flue linings such as was shown in Fig. 3 cannot be depended upon for any length of time. The unlined flue is rough and therefore tends to gather soot. This accumulation of soot in time becomes so great that the flue area is considerably reduced, preventing adequate draft. Brickwork and

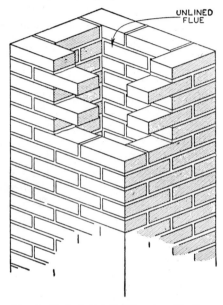

Fig. 3. Typical, Small Chimney with One Unlined Flue

mortar disintegrate when exposed to the action of fuel gases. This disintegration, combined with that occurring naturally from changes in temperature, frequently will cause cracks in the masonry, thereby reducing the effectiveness of the draft. The accumulation of soot in flues is a fire hazard since it is always subject to burning. If there are cracks or loose mortar in the chimney, the fire can easily attack surrounding structural parts and cause serious damage. Many roof fires are caused in this manner. Because an unlined flue is rough, it also has a tendency to reduce the effectiveness of the draft, since the fumes and gases are subject to friction or resistance. A flue lining should always be used when building a chimney but if for any reason one is not used, the walls of the chimney should be made 8″ in thickness instead of 4″ as was shown in Fig. 3.

Flue linings should always be used for chimneys serving gas-fired heating appliances. These linings should be in the form of fire clay liners such as shown in Fig. 4 or of brick made from fire clay. The products of combustion from gas burners contain a large volume of water vapor and some acids. These condense on the inside walls of the flues because of the comparatively low temperature of the masonry. The penetration of this moisture and acid may cause efflorescence and discoloration. As a result, mortar joints will deteriorate rapidly.

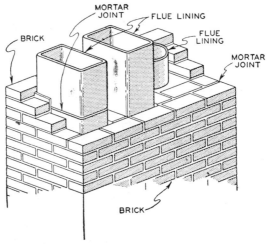

Fig. 4. Large Chimney with Three Lined Flues

Chimneys with lined flues such as shown in Fig. 4 are far superior to those with unlined flues. The cost of flue lining is not great, since, when it is used, the chimney walls need be only 4″ in thickness, except near the top, instead of 8 inches. Lined flues are smooth. Because of this, they will not accumulate soot and are thus not a fire hazard.

Flues should be built as straight as possible. However, it is sometimes necessary to build them with what is called an *offset*, as shown in Fig. 15. Inasmuch as offsets make the flues turn at an angle for some distance before straightening out, they greatly increase the friction, have a tendency to collect soot, and generally decrease the draft. If offsets are necessary, as sometimes happens, especially in the chimneys of residences (see Figs. 1 and 2), their slope should not exceed

30° from the vertical and the full area of the flue should be maintained throughout.

Round flues are more efficient than rectangular ones because the fumes and gases ascend in a spiral. Thus, the products of combustion meet with less friction in a round flue than in a rectangular one. A rectangular flue is not effective over its full transverse area. The column of rising fumes and gases, being nearly circular in cross section, does not fill the corners. However, rectangular flues are cheaper to build and therefore are more generally used.

CHIMNEY MATERIALS. Chimney walls may be built of brick, stone, or solid concrete masonry units. Flue linings should be made of fire clay if at all possible.

Brick. A good, hard-burned, common brick is suitable for brick chimneys. However, for parts of the chimney which are visible, face brick should be used for exterior courses. For chimneys not having a regular flue lining, fire-clay bricks should be used to build the flues. Firebrick resist heat and temperature changes much more readily than ordinary brick.

FLUE LININGS. Flue linings must withstand rapid fluctuations in temperature and at the same time be resistant to the action of ordinary flue gases. The shapes used should be of fire clay with shells not less than 5/8″ in thickness, and should be vitrified. Only sound flue linings should be used.

SEPARATE FLUES. Each device served by a chimney should have an entirely separate flue. This means that there should be a flue for the furnace, another flue for the fireplace, and still another flue for the gas water heater. If more than one device is connected to the flue, the draft for each device is cut approximately in half. As an illustration of this fact, please

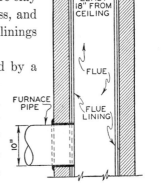

Fig. 5. Two Intake Openings in One Flue

note Fig. 5. Here a stovepipe and furnace pipe enter the same flue. The draft for the furnace will be seriously cut down because the suction which is created by the rising fumes and gases will tend to draw a considerable amount of air through the stovepipe instead of drawing it through the furnace pipe. This reduces considerably the efficiency of the furnace. The same explanation applies to flues for fireplaces. The only exception to the rule is where one flue might serve two small gas appliances such as water heaters without lowering efficiency. This rule is recommended to all masons engaged in the building of chimneys. Separate flues are worth while over and above the additional costs of chimneys.

Chimneys and Flues. It is good practice when designing and erecting chimneys to assume that soft coal will be used as fuel. If this is done, the flue size will be adequate to handle the results of the combustion of any fuel since soft coal produces the most smoke and soot and therefore requires the greatest flue area. All other fuels require less flue area so, by planning on the use of soft coal, a comfortable margin of safety exists if it is not used. This practice makes certain that any type of fuel can be used.

Interior and Exterior Chimneys. Chimneys that are built inside the structure they serve and are not exposed to outside air except near their tops are called *interior chimneys*. Chimneys that are built so that all or the greatest portion of them are exposed to outside air are called *exterior chimneys*.

The walls and flues of an interior chimney, being entirely within the buildings they serve, are always warm. This adds to the efficiency of such chimneys because the ascending fumes and gases retain their heat and thus maintain a steady rise. On the other hand, because exterior chimneys have so much of their outer surfaces exposed to the outside air, cold weather reduces the temperature of chimney walls and flues which in turn reduces the temperature of the ascending fumes and gases. This cooling of the gases causes them to ascend less rapidly which in turn tends to reduce the draft. Thus, the exterior chimney is the less efficient of the two.

Exterior chimneys can be made more efficient by increasing the thickness of all walls which are exposed to the outside air. This will add greatly to chimney costs but is recommended nevertheless.

Chimney Resistance to Weather. The sections of interior chimneys which extend above roofs are subject to wind, rain, and frost. To protect these sections against the elements, proper precautions must be taken in their design and erection. Otherwise, chimneys in time will become unsafe. Most ordinary interior chimneys have walls which are 4″ in thickness. If flue linings are used, the 4″ thickness will be sufficient except for the part directly under and above the roof. Near the roof line, however, chimneys will tend to crack due to wind pressure during hard storms unless they are strengthened. This cracking occurs in the joints between the bricks. It makes chimneys structurally unsafe and they are likely to fall apart above the roof line. If flue linings have not been used, such cracking constitutes a dangerous fire hazard since sparks can easily pass through the opened joints and attack the woodwork of roofs. Rains and freezing temperatures also tend to loosen mortar joints as much as wind pressure.

In order to avoid these dangers, the wall thickness of interior chimneys is increased just under and above the roof line to at least 8″, as shown in Fig. 6. The thicker wall adds stability and overcomes any tendency for cracking resulting from wind pressures and rain combined with freezing temperatures.

All exterior chimneys should have walls at least 8″ thick. The design of such chimneys should be made by a structural engineer to insure their being safe from structural fault disposed to failure.

Exterior chimneys with less than four walls exposed to the outside air should have 8″ walls for each exposed area. Even if chimneys are parts of exterior building walls, their exposed sides should be 8″ walls.

Insulation.   All wood construction adjacent to chimneys should be insulated against fire. Even with flue linings, chimneys may develop one or more cracks due to unexpected settlement, severe winds, or other causes. The greatest care in erection will not completely eliminate this hazard. Therefore, a space of at least 2″ should be left between the outside faces of chimneys and all wooden beams and joists. This space should be filled with a porous, nonmetallic, incombustible material as shown in Fig. 7. The filling should be done before the floor is laid as it not only forms a fire stop but also prevents accumulation of shavings and other combustible material. Baseboards fastened to plaster which is in direct contact with the outside wall of the chimney should be protected by placing a layer of fireproof material at least 2″ in thickness between the chimney wall and the plaster, as shown in Fig. 7. Under no circumstances should wood studding, furring, or lathing be placed

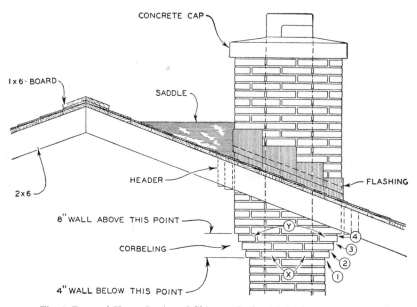

Fig. 6. Exposed Upper Section of Chimney Built with Eight-Inch Walls to Resist Weathering

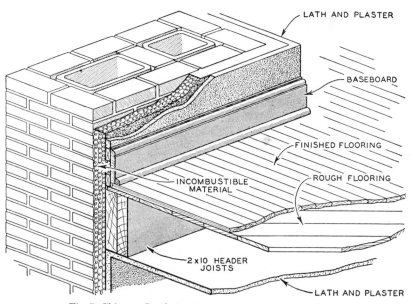

Fig. 7. Chimney Insulation Required in Wood Frame Houses

against a chimney. It is recommended that a coat of cement plaster be applied directly upon the masonry of chimneys which are to be encased by a wood partition or other combustible construction.

Chimney Connections. The connections between smoke pipes and chimneys should be carefully built to assure proper functioning and safety from fire. All openings for chimneys should consist of metal thimbles, around which the chimney brickwork should be carefully laid and cemented. Examples of the thimble and its use are shown in Fig. 8. The smoke pipes should fit tightly in the thimbles. If necessary, boiler clay or putty can be used to make the connections between the smoke pipes and thimbles airtight.

If furring is used on the thimble sides of brick chimneys, the thimbles should be installed by extending the bricks out around the thimbles. This construction is shown in (A) of Fig. 8. Where no furring is to be used, the thimbles are installed as shown at (B) in Fig. 8. Care should be taken to see that the thimbles are installed horizontally.

Note that in (B), of Fig. 8, the smoke pipe extends too far into the flue. The correct installation is shown at (A).

Soot Pockets. Soot pockets, which are shown in (A) and (B) of Fig. 8, should be provided for each range flue. Their use prevents soot accumulations from entering smoke pipes. These pockets need not be more than 8″ to 10″ below the smoke pipes. Such shallow pockets can easily be cleaned out once a year by removing the smoke pipes. If the soot pocket is made much deeper, it will be impossible to remove all of the soot at the cleaning time and the pocket then becomes a fire hazard.

It is advisable to extend the pockets for furnace flues to a point near the base of the chimney where cleanout doors should be provided as shown in Fig. 2. Such doors should be of metal construction. They should fit snugly and be kept tightly closed so that they do not admit any air to the flues. Such soot pockets should be lined the same as the other parts of the flue.

Flashing. Sheet metal flashings around chimneys where they pass through roofs have three general purposes. First, they provide a 2″ clearing around chimneys to allow for expansion due to temperature changes, settlement, or the slight movement of chimneys during severe winds. Second, they provide protection against fire. Finally, they help to make the junctions between roofs and chimneys watertight. Obviously enough, flashing is an important aspect of chimney construction.

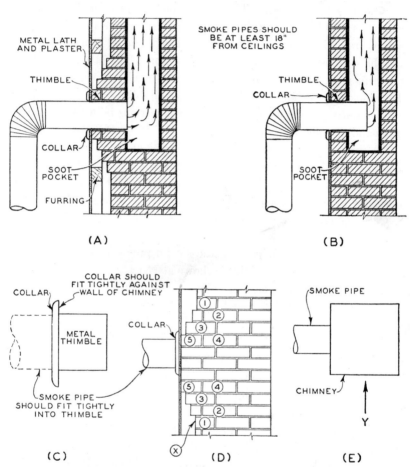

Fig. 8. Typical Smoke Pipe and Chimney Connections

Figs. 9 and 10 show flashing around a typical three-flue chimney. Since this chimney extends through a sloping roof, a *cricket* (sometimes called a saddle) is necessary. This is shown in detail in Fig. 10 and can be seen also in Figs. 6 and 9. The cricket is a means of shedding water around a chimney. Note how the counterflashing is built into the joints between the bricks at *F* and *L* in Figs. 9 and 10. Note also that the sheet metal H over the cricket extends under the shingles K for at least 4″ and is counterflashed as shown in L of Fig. 10. Base flashing B, C, D, and E is lapped by cap flashing A, F, and G in Fig. 9, providing watertight construction. A full bed of mortar should be provided where cap flashing is inserted between bricks.

Corrosion-resistant metal such as copper, zinc, galvanized iron, or lead is the best material to use for flashings. If tin-coated steel is used for flashing, it should be well painted on both sides.

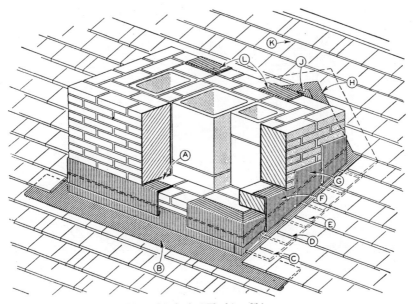

Fig. 9. Method of Flashing Chimney

Spark Arresters.   Spark arresters are more or less desirable where chimneys are near forests, lumber piles, or combustible roofs, depending on the kind of fuel, waste materials, or refuse that may be burned and the amount of deposits that may accumulate in the flues. While spark arresters cannot be depended on entirely to eliminate the discharge of sparks under all conditions, yet, when properly built and installed, they materially reduce the hazards from flying sparks, and are worth many times their cost of installation.

In general, all parts, whether of wire, expanded metal, or perforated sheets, give longer service if they are rust-resistant material. Arresters for residences should have vertical sides extending upward not less than 9″ to provide a gross surface area at least twice that of the flue cross-section area. They should be kept outside the flue area and be securely anchored to the chimney tops. Openings in the screen not less than ⅝″ nor smaller than ⁵⁄₁₆″ in diameter are advisable.

Chimney Finish above Roofs. While common bricks are perfectly satisfactory for all hidden sections of interior chimneys, the use of face

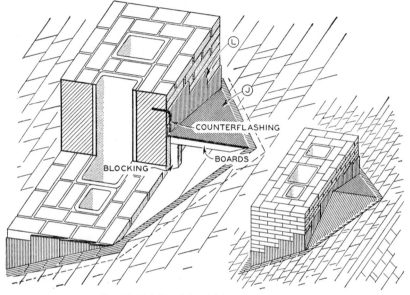

Fig. 10. Details of the Cricket Shown in Fig. 9

brick is advised for all exposed sections, as, for example, that above the roof. Face brick is much harder than common brick and resists weather better. Furthermore, it makes a much better appearance. Chimneys built of solid concrete units can be topped with face brick as a means of adding to the appearance of an otherwise drab, uninteresting structure.

Chimney Caps. To avoid frequent repairs, it is advisable to finish off the tops of chimneys with a durable material such as stone or concrete. The tops of chimneys are especially susceptible to weathering caused by rain, wind, freezing, and sharply changing temperatures.

Fig. 11 shows a simple but typical cap for one-flue chimneys. Note that the concrete portion of the cap should project beyond the chimney walls to prevent rain water from entering the joint between the cap and the chimney walls. This projection also adds to the appearance of the completed chimney. Also note that the flue lining should extend above the top of the concrete portion of the cap from 2 to 4 inches. The flue lining is surrounded with cement mortar to a depth next to the flue lining of about 2 inches. This mortar should be sloped from the sides of the flue to the edges of the concrete as shown by the plan and elevation views. This slope is required to direct air currents upward at the top of the flue linings and also, to drain water away from the flues. Fig. 6 shows a typical chimney cap for a three-flue chimney.

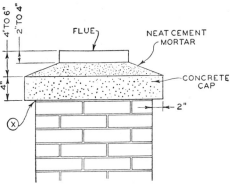

ELEVATION

KINDS OF CHIMNEYS

Single-Flue Interior Chimneys.
Many residences and most stores and apartment buildings require chimney service only from central heating plants. Also, many

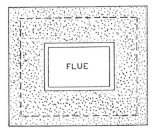

PLAN

Fig. 11. Concrete Cap Used on Single-Flue Chimneys

farm homes and summer cottages require but one chimney for cook stoves or ranges. In such cases, one-flue chimneys serve the purpose satisfactorily.

MATERIALS FOR ONE-FLUE INTERIOR CHIMNEYS. Probably the most common material used for building chimneys is brick masonry. Brick masonry is popular for several reasons. Bricks are easily obtained in practically all parts of the country. Brick sizes are well adapted to work perfectly with standard flue linings. Brick structures are strong and reliable. Finally, bricks can be obtained in a variety of rich shadings which contribute to the natural beauty of buildings in which they are used.

Chimney brickwork should be laid with cement and lime mortar as such mortar is more resistant to the action of heat and flue gases. A good mortar to use in setting flue linings and all chimney masonry except firebrick consists of one part Portland cement, one part hydrated lime, and six parts clean sand, measured by volume. Slaked-lime putty may be used in place of hydrated lime. Firebrick is at its best when laid in fire clay.

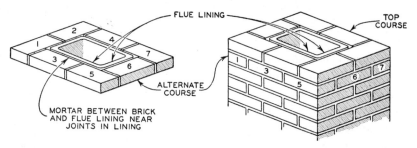

Fig. 12. Typical Chimney

The section view in Fig. 3 and in Figs. 5 and 8 all show typical, one-flue brick masonry chimneys.

Two-Flue Interior Chimneys.   In many instances residences have a fireplace in addition to a furnace. In such cases two flues are required. In situations as found in farmhouses where both a furnace and range are required, again, two flues are needed.

Fig. 13 is an elevation view of a chimney in a typical farm residence having a furnace in the basement and a kitchen range on the first floor. Vertical parallel lines composed of short dashes indicate the furnace and range flues. Note that a concrete footing is used and that the walls of the chimney are 4″ thick. The walls are doubled in thickness above the roof, however, and flue linings are used. The furnace flue has a cleanout, the range flue has a soot pocket, thimbles are provided at both intakes, and the cap at the top of the chimney is an approved design. This is another well-designed chimney. If it is properly built it will serve the residence with but little care required.

MATERIALS FOR TWO-FLUE INTERIOR CHIMNEYS.   Brick masonry is equally applicable to the two-flue chimney. The same mortar is recommended. Fig. 14 shows a section of the chimney illustrated in Fig. 13. The arrangement of the bricks and flue linings is typical.

Three-Flue Interior Chimneys. Residences occasionally have one or more small gas-burning appliances such as water heaters in addition to a fireplace and furnace. Figs. 1 and 2 illustrated this situation.

MATERIALS FOR THREE-FLUE INTERIOR CHIMNEYS. The materials described and recommended for one- and two-flue chimneys are used for three-flue chimneys.

Single-Flue Exterior Chimneys. Single-flue chimneys, except those built for summer cottages, are seldom used for exterior chimneys because they are

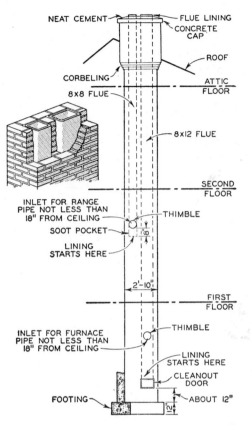

Fig. 13. Elevation View of Chimney for Farm Residence, Showing Flues

not large enough to have pleasing proportions. To build such a chimney larger merely for ornamentation would be prohibitively expensive.

Two- and Three-Flue Exterior Chimneys. There are two general reasons why exterior chimneys of one kind or another having two or more flues are employed for buildings such as residences. First, a chimney having more than two flues is of necessity large, and will take up a great deal of floor space. In addition to this, there is always the problem of where to place such a large chimney without seriously interfering with room arrangements. Second, where a large chimney is required, it can be used to good advantage as decoration or as part of the artistic design of the residence or other building it serves.

MATERIALS FOR TWO- AND THREE-FLUE EXTERIOR CHIMNEYS. A variety of masonry materials, either alone or in combination, can be used for an exterior chimney, the main bulk of which extends out of the residence. Although stone, concrete, and stucco may be used as materials in the construction of chimneys, brick is probably the most popular material used. Some very beautiful chimneys can be designed and built using this type of masonry.

Chimneys with Offsets. Sometimes it is necessary to change the vertical direction of the chimney slightly because of one or more archi-

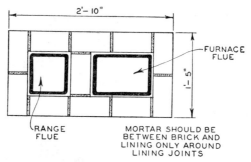

Fig. 14. Section above Range Intake of Two-Flue Interior Chimney

tectural considerations. This change of direction is called an *offset*. Fig. 15 shows an unlined offset in (A) and one that is lined in (B). In the interests of structural safety, the amount of offset must be limited so that center line XY of the upper flue will not fall beyond the center of the wall of the lower flue. Note that when offsetting an unlined chimney, the offsetting begins and ends two courses earlier in the wall toward which the flue is offset. In (A) of Fig. 15, it is the left wall which begins its offset first. The reason for this is to maintain the same area throughout the flue offset after plastering.

Purpose of Chimneys. In general, chimneys have two main purposes. Everyone is familiar with the chimney as the outlet in a structure through which are carried away fumes and other unconsumed gases (smoke) resulting from the combustion of all types of fuels. Unless they are disposed of properly, such fumes and gases are injurious to the health of occupants of buildings and in addition constitute a fire hazard. These fumes must be carried off in such a way as to provide insulation for the structural parts of the building against fire and high enough to be dissipated harmlessly into wind and air. Few people, however, are familiar with a second important function of the chimney. It serves to create a *draft*.

In addition to these two main purposes of the chimney, there are secondary considerations concerning ornamentation and structural sup-

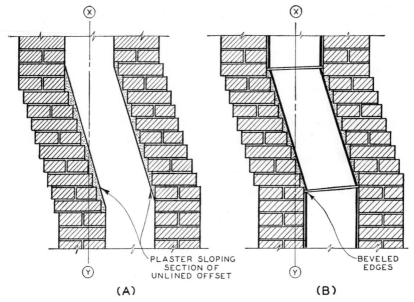

Fig. 15. Chimney Offsets without Lining (A), and with Lining (B)

port. In many cases, and especially in residences, chimneys form a part of the artistic design. Occasionally they are the principal feature of that design.

DESIGN OF CHIMNEYS

Foundations.   Every chimney must have a foundation of sufficient size to provide ample support. This support is necessary to prevent settlement and other obvious difficulties.

The finding of the approximate total weight of a chimney is simply a matter of determining the total cubage of the masonry and multiplying that figure by the weight of the masonry per cubic foot. For general purposes all cubage calculations can be estimates more or less so long as the possible error is on the safe side.

As a means of illustrating the method of finding the weight of a particular chimney, it will be assumed that the weight must be found of the chimney shown in section in Fig. 14, height 30′0 inches.

The cross-section dimensions are 2′10″ x 1′5 inches. For ease in calculating, these dimensions will be called 3′0″ x 1′6 inches. Note that the dimensions were *increased* to the nearest convenient dimension. Then $3 \times 1\frac{1}{2}$ feet $= 4\frac{1}{2}$ feet. The large flue has an inside dimension of 8″ x 12″ and the small one $8\frac{1}{2}$″ x $8\frac{1}{2}$″, or 96 and 72.25 square inches respectively. This makes a total of 168 square inches. One square foot contains 144 square inches. Again, for ease in calculation and to be on the safe side, assume the area of both flues to be one square foot. Then, $4\frac{1}{2} - 1 = 3\frac{1}{2}$ square feet which is the area of the masonry work in the section of chimney under consideration. Multiplying $3\frac{1}{2}$ by 30 equals 105 cubic feet. If brick masonry, including the flue lining, is assumed to weigh 130 pounds per cubic foot, the total weight of the chimney is 105×130, or approximately 14,000 pounds.

This method of calculating the weight of a chimney is used only where the chimney has the same over-all dimension from top to bottom. For fireplace chimneys and where chimneys are enlarged at the top, such as the chimney in the sketch in Fig. 16, the weight of each different section must be calculated separately.

For example, the portion of chimney top between points *AB* in Fig. 16 is treated in the same manner as described for the chimney shown in Fig. 14. The area, cubage, and weight are found, assuming the height dimension starts where the corbeling begins and extends to include the concrete cap. Chimney portion *BC* is handled in the same way described for Fig. 14. Portions *CD* and *DE* are assumed to have the same flue areas as sections *AB* and *BC*. The areas of the fireplace and ashpit are disregarded. The total of all the section weights is the weight of the chimney.

Unlined and Lined Flue Sizes. Before a chimney can be designed or redesigned, the type of heating plant, grate area, and kind of fuel to be burned must be known. This information is necessary because the dimensions of the flues depend principally upon these three points.

Manufacturers of heating equipment occasionally supply, or will supply upon request, information concerning flue sizes and chimney heights which they know is necessary in order that their equipment will function to the best advantage. When such specifications are not available, the chimney design is made on the basis of what is known concerning the heating plant to be used, grate size, and fuel.

In many sections of the country in recent years there has been a tendency to design flues which are suitable only for use with piped fuels. While this may seem economical since a smaller flue will serve such fuels satisfactorily, it could result eventually in unwarranted expenditures. If for one reason or other the supply of piped fuels became unavailable and a change to coal was necessary, the small flues would not be adequate and it would be necessary to rebuild the chimneys. To prevent such needless expense, chimneys should be designed to fit the needs of soft coal. Such chimneys will meet the needs of any fuel.

In this chapter the use of flue lining has been assumed as standard practice. However, the explanations given apply equally well to unlined flues.

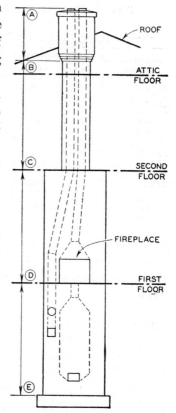

Fig. 16. Elevation for Fireplace Chimney in a Residence

Table I shows the dimensions of commonly used rectangular and round standard commercial flue lining. The rectangular sizes less than 8½″ x 8½″ are frequently employed as vents for gas-fired water heaters and other such appliances. The round sizes less than 8″ in diameter are generally used for the same purpose. Manufacturers of such appliances will supply information concerning required flue sizes.

Table II shows sizes of flue linings and chimney heights recommended for flat-grate furnaces burning soft coal.

Note that Table II is based on various elevations. The term "elevation" means the distance above sea level. For example, Chicago, Illinois, is about 600 feet above sea level, whereas Denver, Colorado, is

TABLE I. DIMENSIONS OF COMMONLY USED STANDARD COMMERCIAL
FLUE LINING

RECTANGULAR LININGS*				ROUND LININGS†			
Outside Dimensions (Inches)	Cross-sectional Area		Wall Thickness (Inches)	Inside Diameter (Inches)	Cross-sectional Area		Wall Thickness (Inches)
	Inside (Sq. In.)	Outside (Sq. Ft.)			Inside (Sq. Ft.)	Outside (Sq. Ft.)	
4½ x 8½.....	23.6	0.26	⅝	6..........	28.3	0.29	⅝
4½ x 13......	38.2	.41	⅝	8..........	50.3	.49	¾
7½ x 7½.....	39.1	.39	⅝	10..........	78.5	.75	⅞
8½ x 8½.....	52.6	.50	⅝	12..........	113.0	1.07	1
8½ x 13......	80.5	.78	¾	15..........	176.7	1.62	1⅛
8½ x 18......	109.7	1.10	⅞	18..........	254.4	2.29	1¼
13 x 13.......	126.6	1.20	⅞	20..........	314.1	2.82	1⅜
13 x 18.......	182.8	1.70	⅞	22..........	380.1	3.48	1⅝
18 x 18.......	248.1	2.30	1⅛	24..........	452.3	4.05	1⅝
20 x 20.......	297.6	2.60	1⅜	27..........	572.5	5.20	2

*All rectangular flue lining is 2′ 0″ long.
†Round flue lining, 6″ to 24″ in diameter, is 2′ 0″ long; that 27″ to 36″ in diameter is 2′ 6″ or 3′ 0″ long.

exactly one mile high. The elevation of any particular locality can be obtained from the offices of the county surveyors or recorders. Elevation is an important factor in offsetting loss in drafts, especially above 4,000 feet.

TABLE II. SIZES OF FLUE LININGS AND HEIGHTS OF CHIMNEYS RECOMMENDED
FOR FLAT-GRATE FURNACES BURNING SOFT COAL

Grate Area (Sq. Ft.)	NOMINAL SIZE OF FLUE LINING IN INCHES								HEIGHT IN FEET OF CHIMNEY TOP ABOVE GRATE AT ELEVATION INDICATED			
	Round (Inside Diameter) at Elevation Indicated				Rectangular (Outside Dimensions) at Elevation Indicated							
	Sea Level	2,000 Feet	4,000 Feet	6,000 Feet	Sea Level	2,000 Feet	4,000 Feet	6,000 Feet	Sea Level	2,000 Feet	4,000 Feet	6,000 Feet
1...	8	8	8	10	8½ x 8½	8½ x 8½	8½ x 8½	8½ x 13	22	26	32	36
2...	10	10	10	10	8½ x 13	8½ x 13	8½ x 13	8½ x 13	24	29	35	41
3...	10	10	12	12	8½ x 13	8½ x 13	13 x 13	13 x 13	26	33	41	49
4...	12	12	12	12	13 x 13	13 x 13	13 x 13	13 x 13	30	37	45	49
5...	12	12	15	15	13 x 13	13 x 13	13 x 18	18 x 18	32	37	43	52
6...	15	18	18	18	18 x 18	18 x 18	20 x 20	20 x 20	30	37	47	56
7...	18	18	18	18	20 x 20	20 x 20	20 x 20	20 x 20	32	41	49	64
8...	18	18	18	18	20 x 20	20 x 20	20 x 20	20 x 20	35	42	56	70

The following notes apply to Table II and to chimneys in general:

1. If anthracite (hard coal) is to be burned exclusively, the required flue area sizes may be reduced by about 25 per cent. However, this is not a recommended procedure as has been pointed out previously.

2. Table II is based on lined flues with no offsets greater than were explained in connection with Fig. 15. However, unlined flues may be included if the joints facing the flues are carefully finished so they are smooth.

3. The smallest sizes of fuels require excessive drafts. Chimneys for them should be made 10 per cent higher.

4. Good design practices advise against using one flue for more than one heating device such as stoves and furnaces. However, if a condition exists requiring that two such devices be served by the same flue, their total grate area may be reduced by 15 per cent. If two gas-fired appliances such as water heaters must be connected to one flue, then the flue should be increased in size at least from 6″ to 8″, or larger if possible.

Table II is also based on grate areas as indicated in the first column on the left-hand side of the table. The manufacturer of any stove, range, or furnace designed to burn coal either shows the recommended grate areas on his equipment or will furnish such information on request. Also, the installers of furnaces will know the grate areas because they must calculate the required grate area for each and every furnace or boiler they install.

Most laundry stoves and kitchen ranges can be served satisfactorily by 8½″ x 8½″ or 4½″ x 13″ rectangular and 8″ round flues.

The sectional area of fireplace flues should have a direct relation to the area of fireplace openings. The area of lined flues should be 12 per cent or more of that of the fireplace opening. If the flues are unlined, the proportion should be increased slightly because of the greater friction. Seventeen square inches of area for chimney flues to every square foot of fireplace opening is a good rule to follow. For example, if a fireplace opening has an area of 8.24 square feet, the sectional area of the required flue should be 140 square inches. It is seldom possible to obtain standard linings of the exact required sectional areas. However, care should be taken to always select linings which are too large rather than too small.

For practice in the determination of the proper size necessary for a particular flue, assume it is desired to know the flue size for a chimney having a grate area of 4½ square feet in which anthracite is to be burned. The furnace is at an elevation of 3,500 feet and a rectangular flue is to be used.

Since the 3,500 elevation is well over 2,000 feet and since Table II is figured only for elevations in multiples of 2,000 feet up to 6,000, it will be assumed that the elevation is an even 4,000 feet. At 4,000 feet, a grate area of 5 square feet, according to Table II, requires a round flue having a diameter of 15 inches. However, when anthracite is used as fuel, it is permissible to reduce the flue size by 25 per cent, assuming that bituminous coal will never be used. The flue size needed will be 11″ in diameter since 25 per cent of 15 is 3.75, or 4, for ease in calculation. Since there is no standard 11″ flue, a 12″ lining will be used.

Suppose that one heating device having a grate area of 3 square feet and another having a grate area of 1½ square feet must be connected to a single flue in a locality 2,000 feet above sea level. What size rectangular or round flue should be used?

Adding the two grate areas gives an answer of 4½ square feet. This total area is reduced by 15 per cent. Thus, the original area of 4½ square feet becomes 3.8 square feet which is the required area. Since the grate sizes in Table II are given only in whole numbers, the nearest whole number, 4, is taken. From Table II it can be seen that for a grate with an area of 4 square feet at an elevation of 2,000 feet, either a 13″ x 13″ square flue or a 12″ diameter round flue will be necessary.

Height of Chimneys.   The higher chimneys are built, the better is the draft they provide. High chimneys are less subject to counter air currents and actually produce stronger and more constant drafts.

Table II also gives the heights recommended for chimneys having various sized flues and located at several different elevations. These heights, while constituting the best possible design, cannot always be used, especially in one-story residences and other small buildings. Therefore, any building being considered should have a chimney designed as near the recommended height as possible with due care being given to the following suggestions:

1. Chimneys should extend at least 3′ above flat roofs and 2′ above the highest ridge of peak roofs.
2. Where chimneys cannot be built high enough above ridges to prevent trouble from eddies caused by the wind being deflected from the roof, hoods may be provided with the open ends parallel to the ridges.
3. Eddies, which force air down the flues, may be caused by erecting chimneys too near adjoining higher buildings. To avoid such possibilities, chimneys should be planned on sides of buildings away from higher buildings or, if this is not possible, the chimneys should be built higher than the top level of the adjoining buildings.

Metal-pipe extensions for chimneys, while not attractive, can be used to increase the height of flues. Such extensions can be provided with metal cowls which turn with the wind and prevent the air from blowing down the flues.

Chimney Locations.   As previously explained, the best location for chimneys is within buildings, since protection against the cold is afforded and the chimney walls, therefore, will always remain warm.

However, because of architectural and utility considerations, such practice is not always possible.

Locating the chimney also requires the consideration of the room arrangements within the building. The best time to plan chimney locations is when the building is being designed. At that time the various rooms and closets can be arranged in the most convenient pattern and the furnace and fireplace locations decided. However, the number and size of the flues must be known before the chimney can be designed or its location planned. The size of the flues can be found by carefully estimating the sizes of the furnace and fireplace and any other heating device.

Chimney Walls. The following material is a summary of the principles which govern the design and construction of chimney walls:

The walls of either interior or exterior chimneys having unlined flues should be 8" thick and the brick constituting the flue lining should be firebrick. The walls of interior chimneys having lined flues can be 4" thick. The walls of exterior chimneys, even with lined flues, should be 8" thick on all sides exposed to outside air. The above-the-roof walls of interior chimneys should be increased to a thickness of 8 inches.

The linings for each flue should be separated by a 4" wythe. Chimney walls around fireplaces should be at least 3" thick. Spaces between brick and flue linings, whether round or rectangular, should be solidly filled with mortar near the lining joints. Unlined flues should be plastered only at offsets.

The foregoing suggestions apply equally well to chimneys built of solid concrete units 4" thick. The walls of chimneys constructed of stone should be at least 12" thick under any conditions.

Solid Chimney Bottoms. Some authorities urge that the bottom portions of chimneys which do not contain fireplaces be composed of solid masonry as a means of giving the chimneys more stability and to distribute the load (weight) more evenly over the foundations. This principle, while making chimneys somewhat more expensive, has merit and could be followed to good advantage.

BUILDING CHIMNEYS

Foundations. The first step in the building of chimneys is the pouring of the concrete footings (also called foundations with respect to chimneys). These footings are an absolute necessity. Before such footings can be poured, their size and location must be accurately determined.

When architects draw the working drawings for small structures, they calculate the correct size for chimneys, their locations, and the size and location of the chimney footings. All such information is shown on the working drawings (blueprints) by dimensions. From the working drawings the mason can quickly determine the footing dimensions and locations.

Locating Chimneys. When the chimney footings are in place, the exact position of the chimney base is outlined on the surface of the footing with chalk, taking the dimensions from the working drawings.

Joint Thicknesses. Joints of $\frac{1}{4}''$ or $\frac{3}{8}''$ are recommended for chimney brickwork. The $\frac{1}{4}''$ joints produce the strongest masonry work. In unlined flues, the joints facing the flues should be struck absolutely smooth and flush with the sides of the bricks so there are no small ledges or other rough places to cause friction or gather soot. The exterior joints for chimneys hidden by structural parts of buildings can be smoothed and made flush with the sides of the brickwork by passing the trowel over them while pressing the trowel against the brickwork. For joints above the roof and for all other brickwork exposed to the weather, the joints should be carefully pointed.

Installing Flue Linings. Chimney flue linings should start at the soot pockets, cleanouts, or above fireplaces (see Figs. 1 and 2) and extend continuously to the cap. The lowest unit of lining in every flue should be supported on at least three sides by brick, solid masonry units, or a stone course projecting from the inside wall of the chimney to the inside wall of the lining. This provides a sure support and prevents any possibility of the lining slipping downward where the joints cannot be repaired.

When the supports for linings are prepared, mortar should be applied at all points where the units of lining will rest. The units of lining should be pressed carefully down on this mortar to insure a firm bed. Care must be taken to see that the joint between the lining and the support is not more than $\frac{1}{2}$ inch. The joints on the inside of the lining must be smoothed and made flush with the surface of the lining so that no small ledges or projections are left.

When the chimney walls have progressed to the top of each unit of lining, the next unit should be placed on the mortar bed on the top of the previous unit and pressed down as previously described. This process is continued to the top of the chimney. In laying up the walls and linings of a chimney, it is advisable to draw a tight-fitting bag of straw up each flue as the work progresses. This will catch any material which might fall into and block the flue.

When necessary, flue lining can be cut by first filling the section with damp sand which is tamped solid. A sharp chisel and light hammer are then used to make small cuts along the line where the cut is to be made. When enough of these small cuts have been made on all sides of the lining, it will finally break cleanly.

When linings are installed in chimney offsets such as shown in Fig. 15, the edges of the linings should be carefully beveled.

Installing Cleanout Doors. When the courses of masonry (brick, concrete units, or stone) are up to the level of the lower edge of the cleanout doors, the doors themselves can be set in place. These doors can be purchased with flanges on all four sides at most building materials yards. A bed of mortar is placed on the masonry and the bottom flanges of the doors pushed into it. The masonry is then placed around and over the other three sides of the doors, making certain that the mortar makes tight joints against all sides of the doors.

Installing Thimbles. When thimbles must be connected to flue linings, the holes in the linings can be cut by using a filling of damp sand as was described for the cutting off of lining units.

Thimbles can be purchased ready to install. The masonry work is built up to the points where the thimbles are to be located and the thimbles placed in position in a good bed of mortar. If brick or stone masonry is being used, individual units can be broken or chipped to fit around the thimbles as the courses are laid. The mortar joints around the thimbles should be tight.

Corbeling. When corbeling is required because of a chimney offset such as shown in Fig. 15, each succeeding brick or course should extend out not more than an inch beyond the course below. The same rule applies to solid concrete units and stone.

When corbeling is required to increase the thickness of chimney walls as shown in Fig. 6, the succeeding courses such as *1, 2, 3,* and *4* should extend out not more than two inches beyond the courses below. Note in Fig. 6 that bricks X and Y have been shortened by cutting. The irregularity of brick lengths in two of the courses is not serious because that portion of the chimney is out of sight under the roof.

It has already been pointed out that when furring is used on the thimble sides of brick chimneys, the brickwork should be extended outward to keep the thimbles from bending. This practice constitutes corbeling. Thimble corbeling is done on only one side of the chimney as shown by the sketch in (D) of Fig. 8. This sketch can be visualized by imagining that the view is taken in the direction of the arrow Y in the smaller sketch at (E).

By studying the sketch at (D) it can be seen that one side of that particular chimney is corbeled out 4″ above and below the thimble and that bricks *1*, *2*, and *3* had to be cut or shortened in order to accomplish the corbeling on the side of the chimney shown. Where the thimble is set, the brick arrangement is as though there were no corbeling at all and the bricks are fitted around the thimble as previously described.

Chimney Caps. Many kinds of concrete chimney caps can be purchased. They are made to fit the needs of chimneys having one, two, and three flues in many varieties of sizes and shapes. In setting a cap, it is placed on the last course of masonry work with a good mortar joint between it and the masonry work. If such ready-made caps are to be used, they must be designed and built to fit the flues and exterior dimensions of the chimneys.

Concrete caps can be made to fit any chimney by making the necessary forms and pouring the concrete. Fig. 17 illustrates a typical made-on-the-job wood form. Such a form can be used for pouring a cap for a two-flue chimney. This form can be made from 1″ boards with slats nailed across the top to keep the flue forms in place. The entire form should be placed on a wood platform and a 1:2:4: concrete mix used for filling it. The mix should be stiff and should be well spaded around the edges of the form. In order to make the visible exterior sides smooth, a mixture of one part cement and one part sand can be pressed against the forms before the regular mix is filled in.

After setting the caps in place, a mixture of equal parts cement and sand is applied on top of the cap and is shaped to the edges of the cap, as shown in Figs. 6 and 11. This should be troweled smooth and firmly against the flues.

Hoods and Pots. It is recommended that a mason who has had considerable experience be consulted regarding the construction of hoods and the installation of pots.

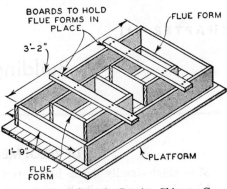

Fig. 17. Wood Form for Pouring Chimney Cap for Two-Flue Chimney

Smoke Test. Every flue should be subjected to a smoke test before the chimney is furred, plastered, or otherwise enclosed. Such a test is conducted by building a paper, straw, wood, or tar paper fire at the base of each flue. When smoke is rising in a dense column, the outlets at the top of the chimney are blocked with a wet blanket. Any smoke escaping through the masonry indicates the location of leaks. Use of this test makes possible the repair of any chance leaks before the chimney is enclosed or put into actual use.

CHAPTER VII

Building with SCR* Brick

DEVELOPMENT

Most single-family homes being erected today have only one-story load-bearing exterior walls. Because of the sizes of standard brick, such houses are ordinarily built with 8″ walls. A wall of that thickness possesses sufficient strength for a three-story structure and is unnecessarily heavy for a dwelling of one story. This is emphasized by the fact that all major national building codes approve 6″ masonry walls for one-story residences.

Many local building codes have long recognized the adequacy of 6″ masonry walls for one-story buildings. With the increasing popularity of this type of construction, additional local codes have extended their approval. A variety of 6″ clay building products have appeared for use in one-story residential and industrial buildings. Some of these are hollow units classed as tile, whereas others are considered as solid units, or brick. In this chapter, we shall treat in some detail a representative example, the SCR brick. The data presented can be regarded as fundamental and applicable to the use of similar products.

The recently introduced SCR brick was developed by the Structural Clay Products Research Foundation. It was designed as a through-the-wall unit requiring no backup material; with it, a nominal 6″ wall can be constructed with a single tier. The SCR brick is intended to adapt masonry construction to present housing design trends at a cost that can compete favorably with other building materials.

DESCRIPTION

As can be seen in Fig. 1, the SCR brick is conventional in appearance; it presents a face outline like that of the standard Norman brick. Its actual dimensions are $2\frac{1}{6}″$ x $5\frac{1}{2}″$ x $11\frac{1}{2}$ inches. When the $\frac{1}{2}″$

---

* Reg. TM "SCPRF"—Pats. Pdg.

allowance for joints is added, the brick has, for construction purposes, a nominal size of 2⅔″ x 6″ x 12 inches. Its weight, when it is of usual composition, is about eight pounds. The unit has ten vertical holes, each 1⅜″ in diameter. The holes constitute less than 25 per cent of the total volume, so the brick is regarded as a solid masonry unit. In one end of each brick, a ¾″ x ¾″ jamb slot is provided to facilitate construction around openings.

Fig. 1. The SCR Brick

PHYSICAL PROPERTIES

Except in size, the SCR brick does not differ from ordinary brick. It is made from the same materials, and by the same processes employed in manufacturing conventional units. The choice of colors will be the same as for standard brick produced by the manufacturer. Single-tier walls of SCR brick have been subjected to the customary laboratory tests with satisfactory results. These included tests for strength, fire resistance, and moisture penetration.

ACCEPTANCE

All nationally recognized building codes permit the use of 6″ masonry for exterior load-bearing walls of one-story single-family homes and private garages. The wall height must not exceed 9′ to the eaves or

15' to the peak of the gables. The same specifications meet the standards of the Federal Housing Administration (FHA). Use of such brick has been endorsed by the Bricklayers, Masons and Plasterers International Union (AFL).

Fig. 2. Brickmason Laying SCR Brick

LAYING THE SCR BRICK

Working with SCR brick does not present any particular problems. The mason may span the entire unit with the hand, as demonstrated in Fig. 2, or, for easier handling, the core holes provide a convenient hold. These same holes help to reduce "floating" of the brick on very wet or plastic mortar. Tests have disclosed that where the maximum transverse strength is desired, mortar Type A-2 $(1:\frac{1}{2}:4\frac{1}{2})$ is to be preferred.

The SCR brick is a modular unit, that is, its dimensions can be taken as a unit of measurement in laying out work. It is most easily used with a stretcher (half) running bond, as shown in Fig. 3. Walls and corners can then be laid using only whole brick. If door and window widths and wall lengths are planned in multiples of 6″ or 12″, only half-units will be required to work around the openings with no attendant

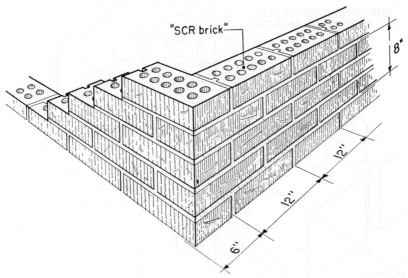

Fig. 3. Simple Wall Construction with SCR Brick

waste of material. Three courses of SCR brick make 8″ of wall height; and 450 units are needed for 100 square feet of wall area.

CONSTRUCTION DETAILS

Wall Construction. A 2″ x 2″ furring strip is recommended for use with SCR brick wall construction. Such furring provision allows ample space for a moisture barrier, and installation of electrical and plumbing equipment, as well as insulation. The 2″ x 2″ stock offers sufficient rigidity to permit anchoring the strips only at three points. Since the strips can be nailed to the top wall plate, only two clips will be required. The special clip shown in Fig. 4 has been devised for use with this construction arrangement. The furring strips are driven onto the staples after the wall is completed. The width of the clip allows the horizontal positions of the staples to be adjusted as needed to align them properly. The clips hold the furring approximately ¼″ away from the masonry; this feature allows air to circulate freely and permits moisture readily to drain down to the weep holes in the bottom course, as can be seen in Figs. 5 and 6.

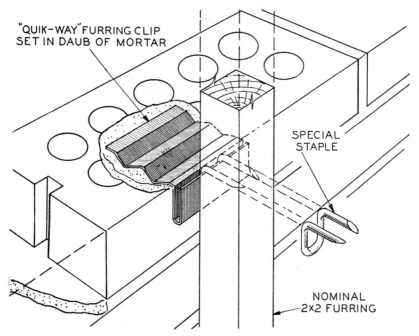

Fig. 4. Furring Clip Designed for Use with SCR Brick Construction

    The space provided by the furring can be insulated in the same manner as in any wall. The cavity is adequate to carry most standard electrical installations and piping. It must be observed, however, that pipes or ducts cannot be cut into single-tier SCR brick walls. Building codes do not permit reducing the nominal thickness of a 6″ wall. Where pipes or ducts cannot be run through the furred-out space, they must be boxed in. For heating systems, special "out-of-wall" and baseboard registers are available.

    Foundations. Laying SCR brick on a standard 8″ foundation requires no special instructions. With slab-on-the-ground building where no basement is to be provided, the wall is very simply erected on the foundation as shown in Fig. 5. In cold climates a rigid mineral insulation should be installed between the floor construction and the exterior foundation wall.

Floor joists cannot be framed into a 6″ masonry wall. If a basement or crawl-space is planned, metal hangers must be installed or the wall must be corbeled out to provide a bearing surface for the joists. The

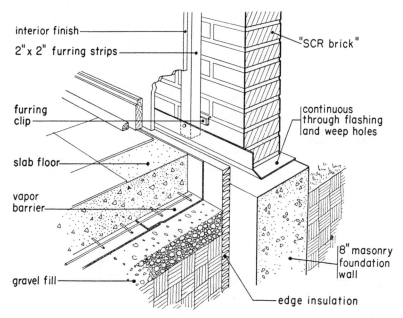

interior finish
2″x 2″ furring strips
"SCR brick"
furring clip
continuous through flashing and weep holes
slab floor
vapor barrier
gravel fill
8″ masonry foundation wall
edge insulation

Fig. 5. Foundation Details with Slab-on-the-Ground Construction

latter arrangement is preferable and one method of doing this is illustrated in Fig. 6. It should be noticed that in all cases the furring strips extend only to within 2″ or 3″ of the floor level. This allows for a gradual curve of the metal flashing to improve drainage to the weep holes.

Because of unusual local conditions in some areas, building regulations may require 10″ or 12″ foundation walls. Simple methods have been worked out to accommodate the SCR brick to such foundations. Fig. 7 shows how the wall can be erected on a 10″ foundation. In this case, the SCR brick are backed up from the grade line to the joist level with masonry 4″ thick. On 12″ foundations, the same procedure may be

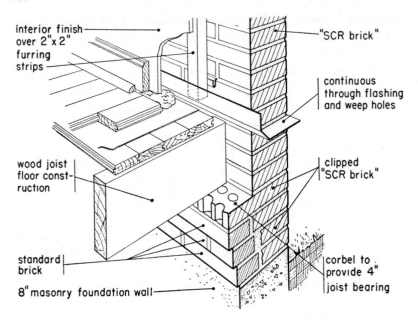

interior finish over 2"x 2" furring strips

"SCR brick"

continuous through flashing and weep holes

clipped "SCR brick"

wood joist floor construction

standard brick

corbel to provide 4" joist bearing

8" masonry foundation wall

Fig. 6. Floor Joists Supported on Corbeled Wall

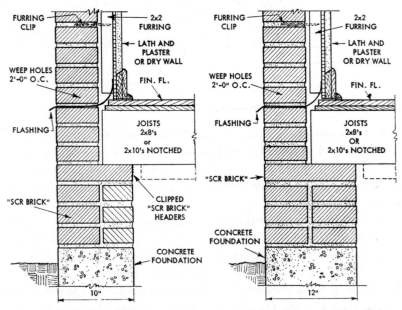

FURRING CLIP

2x2 FURRING

LATH AND PLASTER OR DRY WALL

WEEP HOLES 2'-0" O.C.

FIN. FL.

FLASHING

JOISTS 2x8's or 2x10's NOTCHED

"SCR BRICK"

CLIPPED "SCR BRICK" HEADERS

CONCRETE FOUNDATION

10"

Fig. 7. Construction on 10″ Foundation

FURRING CLIP

2x2 FURRING

LATH AND PLASTER OR DRY WALL

WEEP HOLES 2'-0" O.C.

FIN. FL.

FLASHING

JOISTS 2x8's OR 2x10's NOTCHED

"SCR BRICK"

CONCRETE FOUNDATION

12"

Fig. 8. Construction on 12″ Foundation

followed if the 2″ "shelf" on the foundation wall is not objectionable. Otherwise, backup units 6″ thick may be used as shown in Fig. 8. Whenever constructing walls two units in thickness, the two tiers of masonry should be carefully bonded together with metal ties, as explained in Chapter II. It should be borne in mind that the limitations upon the height of 6″ walls applies only to that part of the construction that is actually only 6″ in thickness.

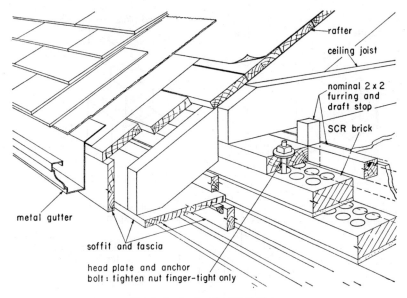

Fig. 9. Anchoring the Head Plate

Head Plate Anchorage. A continuous 2″ x 6″ head plate is anchored to the SCR brick wall by means of anchor bolts, in the manner shown in Fig. 9. When the units are laid with stretcher bond, the core holes line up and no cutting is necessary to locate the anchor bolts. The depth to which the bolts must enter the wall is regulated by local codes, but should never be less than three courses of brick. If ⅜″ bolts are used, they should be spaced no more than four feet apart; ½″ bolts may be eight feet apart. The bolts pass through the core holes and, by staggering their positions, bowing of the head plate will be prevented. The anchor bolt nuts are to be tightened with the fingers and a wrench should never be used on them. Since the furring strips are nailed to the head plate, it should extend about ¼″ beyond the inside edge of the wall, to properly line up with the strips.

Doors and Windows. Using SCR brick, lintels may be designed in several ways, as shown in Fig. 10. When reinforced brick lintels are used, care must be taken that the construction details have been accurately computed to safely bear the load over the opening. Where steel lintels are used, the horizontal width must be 6 inches. In some cases

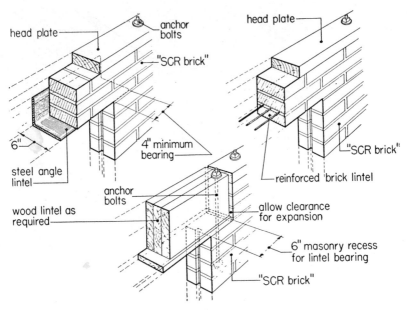

Fig. 10. Three Methods of Lintel Construction

it may be desirable to employ all frame construction above the height of the openings. Fig. 11 shows a residence designed in this fashion.

Installation of doors and windows in SCR walls raises no unique problems. Stock items can usually be selected that will not necessitate any unusual cutting of brick. The fin of a steel window frame fits into the jamb slot of the brick as shown in Fig. 12. Installation of a wood window frame is illustrated in Fig. 13, with the blind stop fitted into the brickwork and the frame anchored in the wall with a buck anchor. Proper calking will make either type of construction weathertight. Standard procedures in placing flashing should be followed.

Fig. 11. A One-Family Residence Constructed with SCR Brick

Door construction details are similar and are illustrated in Fig. 14. A ¾″ strip is fastened to the rough buck and installed in the slot of the brickwork. The addition of calking insures a positive weather stop to prevent the entrance of wind or water. The rough buck is securely held in place by anchor strips in the joints of the masonry. After completion

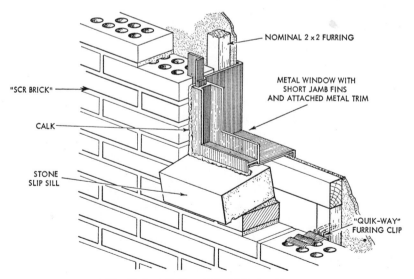

Fig. 12. Installation of Steel Window Frame

of the brickwork, the finished door frame is set in position in the ordinary way.

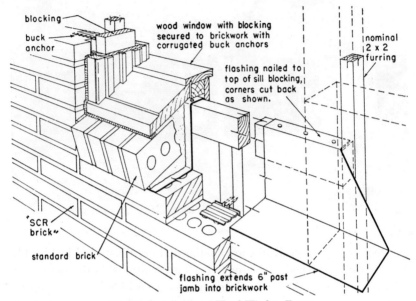

Fig. 13. Installation of Wood Window Frame

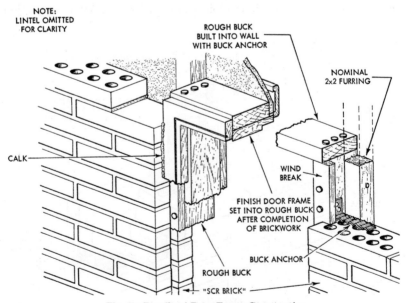

Fig. 14. Details of Door Frame Construction

INDEX